Lullabies OF THE WORLD

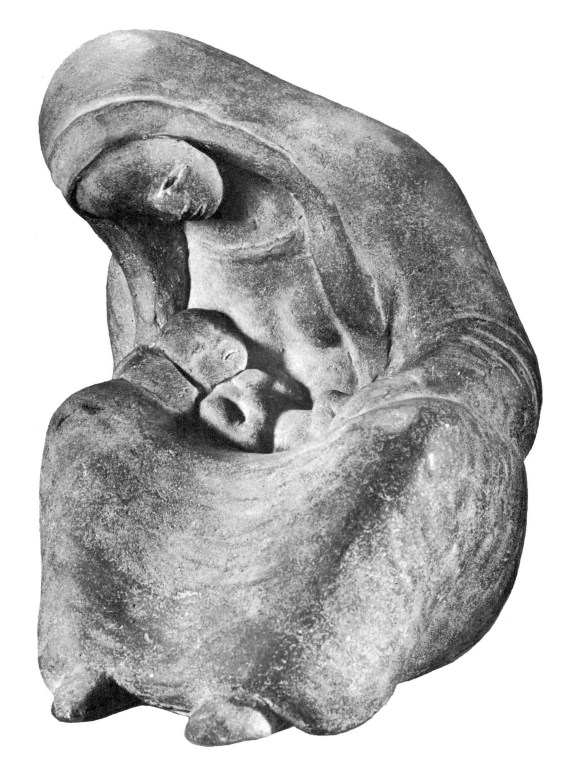

Lullabies OF THE WORLD

DOROTHY BERLINER COMMINS

RANDOM HOUSE INC. · NEW YORK · MCMLXVII

CUMBERLAND COUNTY COLLEGE
LIBRARY P.O. BOX 517 VINELAND N.J.

Dver
M
1997
C73
L83

68-10,163

The author is deeply grateful to
P. J. CONKWRIGHT
for the distinguished design of this book

Some of these lullabies appeared in LULLABIES OF MANY LANDS, collected and arranged by Dorothy Berliner Commins.
Copyright, 1941, by Artists and Writers Guild, Inc.
Permission to reprint the following is gratefully acknowledged:
"Nightingale with the Black Beak," "Hush-a-bye, My Lovely Child"
from FOLKSONGS OF EUROPE, by permission of Novello & Co., Ltd.
"Lullaby, My Jamie," by permission of Breitkopf & Hartel, Weisbaden.
"Little Red Bird of the Black Turf," by permission of Stainer & Bell, Ltd.
"Sleep, Sleep, My Child," from Journal of the Folk Song Society, 1911, No. 16,
by permission of the English Folk Dance & Song Society.
"Sleep on Till Dawn," by permission of Curwen & Sons, Ltd.
"Nani, Nani, Mother's Little Baby" from BULGARIAN-MACEDONIAN FOLK MUSIC, by Boris A. Kremeniliev,
by permission of the University of California Press.
"Whose Child Is This Baby?" from SONGS OF THE AKAN PEOPLE, by Isaac D. Riverson (Methodist Book Depot,
Cape Coast, Ghana) by permission of Isaac D. Riverson.
"Sleep, Sleep, My Handsome Son" from CHANTS JUDEO-ESPAGNOLS, by Isaac Levy
(World Sephardi Federation, London) by permission of Isaac Levy.
"Lali, Keshav's Lali" from MUSIC OF HINDUSTAN, by A. H. Fox Strangways, by permission of Clarendon Press.
"Go to Sleep, Little Sister" from CHANT CAMBODGIENS, collected by George de Gironcourt,
by permission of Librairie Fischbacher.
"Little One, Oh Little One, Go to Sleep" from FOLKSONGS OF THE VISAYAS, by permission of
Silliman Music Foundation, Inc., The Philippines.
"Though Shadows Dark," by permission of G. Schirmer, Inc. Copyright, 1937, by G. Schirmer, Inc.

First Printing
© Copyright, 1967, by Dorothy Berliner Commins
All rights reserved under International and Pan-American Copyright Conventions.
Published in New York by Random House, Inc., and simultaneously
in Toronto, Canada, by Random House of Canada Limited.
Library of Congress Catalog Card Number: 67-22645
Manufactured in the United States of America

IN MEMORY OF

Mother and Saxe

I DEDICATE THIS BOOK

TO THE CHILDREN

OF THE WORLD

CONTENTS

FOREWORD

*L*ullabies are love songs. Sometimes they are gay and sometimes they are sad; but, whatever the mood, they are always tender. They are the expression of one of the deepest emotions of the human spirit. A lullaby is born in a mother's heart to live on in the child's memory, for a lifetime and even longer; for lullabies are passed on from generation to generation.

The world today is changing swiftly. No pattern of family life in any part of the world can be definitive. Lives do not set like concrete, nor is folklore cast in bronze. The characteristic of folk music has been its flexibility, its power to keep an identity while borrowing and assimilating elements from other cultures. Today diverse and distant cultures touch upon each other, for technological development has made time, distance, and natural barriers dwindle.

One day we may find ourselves members of one world. This will be only the fulfillment of the human condition; for, in a real sense, there has been one world since the beginning of human history, the family of man. Mother love is universal. It survives in folk lullabies all over the world. Though cultures may change, nations rise and fall, languages evolve or vanish, there will always be lullabies. This collection is designed to preserve something of the past and at the same time to look forward to the future.

To the child in the cradle or the mother's arms, these love songs are the first melodies heard. They are sung at an hour when the mother's presence and the sound of her voice mean safety and peace and comfort. While the mother rocks her child back and forth, old melodies are recalled and return. She sings what she remembers hearing as a baby, what her mother sang to her, and her mother's mother. New words are added. Slight changes in the melody occur, but the substance and the spirit are unchanging.

The character of most lullabies can be identified with the history of a people. They belong to no composer. They belong to all mothers of a nation or a culture. Like all folklore, the lullaby came into being spontaneously. Need for it gave it birth, and it flowered with a vitality all its own. It has always been so with folklore, whether the form of expression is a nursery rhyme, a fairy tale, an epic or a legend. The first tellers of tales and singers of songs will be forever unknown. Much must have been lost and much must have been gained as the new, added to the old, kept alive the folk song and story. The familiar analogy to the tree in the forest is apt. From year to year its fruit is plucked or falls; its leaves are shed, and often branches wither away or are struck down. But the sturdy tree has deep roots in the soil, representing the past. New seasons continually bring new branches, new leaves, blossoms, and fruit.

Of all folklore, the lullaby may have the simplest and most direct appeal. It needs no words, and even when words are used, the infant is usually too young to understand them. The sounds and rhythms suffice. Whatever the words mean, it is the mother alone who really appreciates them. The thought of a cradle swaying perilously on a treetop would only terrify an infant. Wind blowing and the whole bough breaking and falling with a crash would probably be good raw material for nightmares if the child really grasped the meaning of the words. What can a Greek baby, for example, know or care about ruling over Alexandria, Cairo, or Constantinople, though the mother blithely promises these to him if he will only go to sleep? Gentle rhythms convey all the meaning he needs at the moment —and all the conquest. However, the words have a very real meaning to the mother. They express the hopes mothers always cherish for their children.

It can be assumed that most lullabies originated among the peasantry and the working classes. Mothers of the aristocracy were seldom required to devote themselves exclusively to their infants. They could easily engage wet nurses and governesses. These servants came from the land and brought with them the traditions and beliefs and songs of the people. They lulled an infant to sleep in their arms while they swayed in gentle, rhythmic movement. And when hands could not be spared from the many chores that fall to the lot of women, the foot-rocking cradle was invented.

Even when cradles are not used (as, for example, in Japan and in some parts of Asia and Africa) the infant is usually strapped to the mother's back so that her hands will be free for work in the fields or at home.

No one, however, could complain that a song interfered with work in progress. The mind can wander free and the voice can rise and fall in tender cadences while the hands are busy. How can one account for the persistent note of great sadness running through the words and melodies of many lullabies? Prospects less than promising exist for many a child in his crib. Since time began mothers have seen their bright dreams for their children shattered. Sons have marched off to wars; others have lived lives of grinding poverty, of hopeless illness and defeat. But equally important are the visions of a better life and happier times which enter into lullabies. Cares are banished and poverty is forgotten. Courage and gaiety replace longing and despair. Even the song shifts in mood. Lightness and charm come into the melody.

A number of the lullabies in this collection have been taken down directly from singers or from tape recordings. It was necessary to create a simple piano setting not only to help establish the mood of each melody, but also to convey something of the spirit and character of songs which come from the far corners of the globe. This has required some adjustment. It is well known that the music of cultures outside the western tradition cannot be considered in a western frame of reference if the artistic values are to remain fully intact. For example, the music of the Far East is not based on an harmonic system. It is linear, and it is the melodic line, replete with decoration, embellishment and often great subtlety, which is most significant. The melodies evolve out of highly complex modal systems, often much more intricate than western modes. Our staff and our system of notation are not designed to catch all the subtleties of pitch and inflection. In every instance, however, an attempt has been made to capture this beautiful expression of the human spirit and to preserve it before it is lost. The lullaby is worthy of a place with all the other treasures of man's endeavor which have been passed on to posterity.

Lullabies OF THE WORLD

Canada

Come to Your Mommy

BEGINNING in the middle of the 18th century, people began to migrate to Canada from England, Scotland, Wales, and Ireland. Though they were like the settlers who came to other parts of America, seeking a new and better way of life, they brought with them and preserved much of their rich legacy of folklore and folk music. As a result, most of the songs sung and cherished by these people can not only be traced back to originals, but are still sung by the people of their homelands. This lovely old melody is widely known in Scotland and in the north of England. No one knows what the original words may have been, but a version in 1806 appeared as "Sing to Your Mam-

my, My Pretty Lammy." In Fordyce's *Newcastle Song-Book* (1842) this melody appeared set by William Watson to verses called "The Little Fishy." One reads:

> "Dance to your Daddy
> My little babby,
> Dance to your Daddy, my little lamb.
> You shall have a fishy
> In a little dishy
> You shall have a fishy,
>   when the boat comes in."

Though there are many versions and variants of the words of this song, each depends on the traditional lullaby promise of good things to come in the future.

COME TO YOUR MOMMY

Come to your mommy,	Ye will get a coatie	Come to your mommy,
My bonnie laddie;	An' a pair o' breekies	My bonnie laddie;
Come to your mommy,	An' a whirligiggie	Come to your mommy,
O my little lamb.	An' a supple tam!	O my little lamb.

She Will Gather Roses

ONE of the special characteristics of the Tsimshian Indians is a complex tribal, clan, and family social structure. Divisions of this tribe spread all over the entire area along the shores of the Nass and Skeena rivers among the Rockies of northwest British Columbia. Thus the lullaby, "She Will Gather Roses," a special song for girls only, belongs to and is used by the family of *Weerhae* (chief family of the Wolf Clans) of *Gitwinl-*

kul. It is a moving melody sung against a background of drum beats. The Tsimshians are noteworthy for their veneration of their ancestors. It becomes the bond of kinship which unites them all, and each clan and sub-clan proudly traces its lineage, both real and mythical. Their sense of order and their deeply felt beliefs permeate their lives with ritual and ceremony and are made manifest in their highly developed arts and crafts.

Tsimshian Indian

haw haw hay hay | hee ___ | Tem | ram sa-ka niht trahl | Kyal kum hanak | Kaw

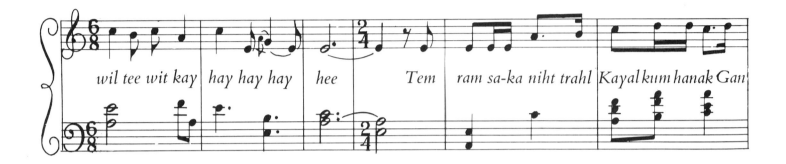

wil tee wit kay | hay hay hay | hee | Tem | ram sa-ka niht trahl | Kayal kum hanak Gan

wiltee wit kay ha | hee ___ | Tem ram sa mi - gunt trahl Kayal kum ha-nak Tem ram kanak

SHE WILL GATHER ROSES

A hay hay hay a hay hay hay a hee
A hay a hay a hay a hay a hee

A hye haye ha ha ha he
Hay hay hay a hee

She will gather roses, the little girl,
That is why she was born.

She will dig up wild rice with her fingers,
the little girl,
That is why she was born.

She will pick strawberries,
That is why she was born.

She will, the little woman,
pick up blueberries,
That is why she was born.

She will pick soapberries,
That is why she was born.

She will pick elderberries,
That is why she was born.

She will gather wild roses,
That is why she was born.

TEMRAM SAKALAMPS

A hay hay hay a hay hay hay a hee
A hay a hay a hay a hay a hee

A hye ha he hay hay ha hay
Hay hay hay a hee

Tem ram sa-ka lamps trahl
Kyal kum hanak

Kan wil tku dee
Wit kul a haw haw hay hay hee

Wit ku a haw haw hay hay hee
Tem ram sa-ka niht trahl

Kyal kum hanak
Kaw wil tee wit kay hay hay hay hee

Tem ram sa-ka niht trahl
Kyal hum hanak

Ganwiltee wit kay ha hee
Tem ram sa migunt trahl

Kyal kum hanak
Tem tahl hanak

Təmqam saqálámps

A he he a he he he a hi
A he a he a he a he a hi

A hye ha ye he he ha he
He he he a hi

Təmqam saqálámps txaɬ
Keɬ k̓um hanáq̓

Qan wil tku di'
Wit kul a ho ho he he hi

Witkᵘ a ho hø he he hi
Təmqam sa'qaníx̱t txaɬ

Keɬ kum hanáq̓
Qan wilti' witkᵘ he he he hi

Təmqam sa 'qaníx̱t txaɬ
Keɬ k̓um hanáq̓

Qan wilti' witkᵘ ha hi
Təmqam samigunt txaɬ

Keɬ kum hanáq̓
Təmtaɬ hanáq̓

5

Dear Boy

THE language of the Tsimshian Indians is an enigmatic problem for linguists. So far they have been unable to relate their language to any other in North America or elsewhere. But their music, especially that of the Tsimshians living in the mountain areas, offers at least hints and clues which indicate a relationship with the Asian peoples on the other side of the Bering Sea, sharing a

similar quality of lyricism and beauty. This lullaby for boys is used exclusively by the family of *Trahahaet,* Chief of the Eagle Clan whose hunting grounds are located at Hyanmas, below the mouth of the Nass river. Some songs of the Tsimshians were used for more than one purpose and sung at gatherings. This one, "Nadu-Nadu," was used exclusively to put a boy to sleep.

ee lawhl hyanmas Damwil- -wil-mukl Wea yae yawhl tem A day ahl tsamqul

hat Tam'am see gyaw Aw tsem ka lep lip. Na - du na du - du Na - du

du na. du du na du na du du ____ ku na _ du na du du na du

na du du na du na du du hu hu ____ na du na du du

DEAR BOY

Dear boy, dear boy, dear little boy
Sit up at night, my sister
Sit up at night with me, O my sister
To make me grow
Till I become a grown man
Then I will go to the large creek
Of my forefathers
To Hyanmas where I will catch
The large spring salmon
Then I will fish at Echo-Cliffs
That is where I will gather
The fish spines
For Thunder-Woman
Dear boy, dear boy, dear little boy.

NATUTU

'Natɿ, natutu, kunátu
'Aɬtade dá'i kwe dǿts
'Aɬtade dá'i kwe dǿts
Mɔ̄dzi səm'áse
Təm' wil-wi qede'
Nedəm wil go' ot
'Wisaget 'aks tə pyéʼi
Loɬ x̱anḿás
Dəmwil-wil mugɬ 'wiye'
Φltəm'a de
Aɬtsəm gul hat
Təm'an si gɷ'
Φ ksəm ga ləp lip
Natɿ, natutu, kunatu

NADUDU

Nadu, nadudu, kunadu
Ahl taday dai kway dawts
Ahl taday daee kway dawts
May dzee sem a say
Tam wil-wee qyae day
Nae dem wil kaw
Aw wee sa raet aks
Tep yae ee lawhl hyanmas
Damwil-wil-mukl
Wea yae yawhl tem
A day ahl tsamqul hat
Tam'an see gyaw
Aw tsem ka lep lip.
Nadu nadudu kunadu

7

It Is a Gray Hen

FRENCH CANADA may be said to have begun in 1504 when Jacques Cartier landed on the Gaspe and claimed the country for France, even though it was more than a hundred years later in 1608 when the first settlers came to stay. They settled in Quebec and have been there ever since. More venturesome souls went beyond and, as trappers, opened up areas for fur trading. Despite the fact that their direct ties with France were severed in the late 18th century when France lost Canada to Britain, they have managed to keep a distinct French-speaking culture of their own even into modern times. They have, as might be expected, preserved the songs of their homeland, most of them dating far back to the songs of the French *jongleurs* in the Middle Ages. And in many cases they have maintained something of the modal quality characteristic of medieval music. Only the first two lines of each stanza change in this lullaby. As the song progresses and, hopefully, the child drifts into sleep, notice how the hens move from realism to a world of dream and fantasy.

IT IS A GRAY HEN

It is a gray hen
Who lays in the church
She will lay a beautiful little egg
For her little one who is going to go to sleep,
She will lay a beautiful little egg
For her little one who is going to go to sleep.
   Sleep, sleep.

It is a white hen
Who lays in the branches
She will lay a beautiful little egg
For her little one who is going to go to sleep,
She will lay a beautiful little egg
For her little one who is going to go to sleep.
   Sleep, sleep.

It is a black hen
Who lays in the cupboard
She will lay a beautiful little egg
For her little one who is going to go to sleep,
She will lay a beautiful little egg
For her little one who is going to go to sleep.
   Sleep, sleep.

It is a green hen
Who lays in the covers
She will lay a beautiful little egg
For her little one who is going to go to sleep,
She will lay a beautiful little egg
For her little one who is going to go to sleep.
   Sleep, sleep.

It is a brown hen
Who lays on the moon
She will lay a beautiful little egg
For her little one who is going to go to sleep,
She will lay a beautiful little egg
For her little one who is going to go to sleep.
   Sleep, sleep.

It is a yellow hen
Who lays in the alder tree
She will lay a beautiful little egg
For her little one who is going to go to sleep,
She will lay a beautiful little egg
For her little one who is going to go to sleep.
   Sleep, sleep.

C'EST LA POULETTE GRISE

C'est la poulette grise
Qui pond dans l'eglise,
Ell' va pondre un beau p'tit coco
Pour son p'tit qui va fair' dodiche,
Ell' va pondre un beau p'tit coco
Pour son p'tit qui va fair' dodo.
   Dodiche, dodo.

C'est la poulette blanche
Qui pond dans les branches,
Ell' va pondre un beau p'tit coco
Pour son p'tit qui va fair' dodiche,
Ell' va pondre un beau p'tit coco
Pour son p'tit qui va fair' dodo.
   Dodiche, dodo.

C'est la poulette noire
Qui pond dans l'armoire,
Ell' va pondre un beau p'tit coco
Pour son p'tit qui va fair' dodiche,
Ell' va pondre un beau p'tit coco
Pour son p'tit qui va fair' dodo.
   Dodiche, dodo.

C'est la poulette verte
Qui pond dans les couvertes,
Ell' va pondre un beau p'tit coco
Pour son p'tit qui va fair' dodiche,
Ell' va pondre un beau p'tit coco
Pour son p'tit qui va fair' dodo.
   Dodiche, dodo.

C'est la poulette brune,
Qui pond dans la lune,
Ell' va pondre un beau p'tit coco
Pour son p'tit qui va fair' dodiche,
Ell' va pondre un beau p'tit coco
Pour son p'tit qui va fair' dodo.
   Dodiche, dodo.

C'est la poulette jaune,
Qui pond dans les aulnes,
Ell' va pondre un beau p'tit coco
Pour son p'tit qui va fair' dodiche,
Ell' va pondre un beau p'tit coco
Pour son p'tit qui va fair' dodo.
   Dodiche, dodo.

Sleep, Sleep, Little One

FOR thousands of years before any white man reached the shores of the New World, Indians and Eskimos roamed the vast spaces which now comprise Canada, and, thus, the song history of Canada begins with them. For Indians all forms of singing had a special religious significance. Since the Great Spirit was invisible, it was believed that song, "invisible voice," could reach the Spirit. So, in a sense, all songs were forms of prayer.

This song is characteristic of the Iroquois Tribe, who inhabited the regions around the St. Lawrence and the Great Lakes. Their songs were usually short and made up of a few words and sometimes, dispensing with words altogether, employed only patterns of sounds and syllables. The lullaby, of course, was of the utmost importance to these people, for it was the infant child's introduction to the whole realm of ritual song.

SLEEP, SLEEP, LITTLE ONE

Sleep, sleep, little one,
Sleep, sleep, little one,
Sleep, sleep, little one,
Now go to sleep, now go to sleep.

HO, HO, WATANAY

Ho, ho, watanay,
Ho, ho, watanay,
Ho, ho, watanay,
Kiyokena, kiyokena.

United States

Rock-a-by Baby, on the Treetop

ALTHOUGH the words of "Rock-a-by-Baby" had long been familiar as a Mother Goose rhyme, the credit for setting these words to music is generally given to Mrs. Effie Canning Carlton, who is said to have composed it on the porch of her father's summer home in 1874. It received widespread popularity when it was used as one of the songs in Denman Thompson's production of *The Old Homestead*. A good deal of controversy, however, attends Mrs. Carlton's claim. Evidence indicates that the melody existed long before Mrs. Carlton joined it to the words to make the lullaby which is now so well known. One story she tells is particularly interesting. She reports that in 1854 her parents found an Indian squaw who had been injured and they took her into their house and nursed her. When the squaw recovered, she took a fancy to the baby of the family and often sang the melody of what we now call "Rock-a-by-Baby." Melodies travel wide and far, invisibly and swifter than words. Perhaps the Indian woman had heard it from some white settler, and it is quite possible that Mrs. Carlton as a child heard this melody in Boston and later lifted it from some vague, unconscious memory. In any case, she honestly believed that it was her own creation and she certainly deserves credit for bringing together melody and words to make one of the most popular of all lullabies.

ROCK-A-BY BABY, ON THE TREETOP

Rock-a-by baby, on the treetop,
When the wind blows, the cradle will rock,

When the bough breaks, the cradle will fall,
And down will come baby, cradle and all.

A Frog He Would A-Wooing Go

THIS song, widely known throughout the land and often recorded by folksingers, has a long history. It dates back at least four centuries, for the story of Mr. Frog's courtship was sung by shepherds in *The Complaynt of Scotland* (1549). By 1580 it had appeared in popular ballad form. In 1611 the music and a text of thirteen verses appeared in Thomas Ravenscroft's third collection of rounds and folksongs—*Melismata*. A version of it is in *Pills to Purge Melancholy* (1720), a famous collection of traditional songs edited by Thomas D'Ur-

fey. From then on, into the middle of the nineteenth century, it appears with undiminished frequency in England. Obviously it came to America with the colonists, and it was used in all parts of the new land, always changing slightly to accommodate the particular environment and being transformed by the individual singer. Here is one version that has reached the nursery and stayed there. It is an extremely functional lullaby because of its many verses. Long before the end most children are sound asleep.

this   is the stor - y   of their romance   m - m   m - m

A FROG HE WOULD A-WOOING GO

A frog he would a-wooing go, m-m, m-m,
A frog he would a-wooing go,
Whether his mother would let him or no, m-m, m-m.

He rode right to Miss Mousie's den, m-m, m-m,
He rode right to Miss Mousie's den,
Said he, "Miss Mousie, are you within?" m-m, m-m.

"Yes, kind Sir Frog, I sit to spin," m-m, m-m,
"Yes, kind Sir Frog, I sit to spin.
Pray, Mister Frog, won't you walk in?" m-m, m-m.

He said, "My dear, I've come to see," m-m, m-m,
He said, "My dear, I've come to see,
If you, Miss Mousie, will marry me?" m-m, m-m.

"I don't know what to say to that," m-m, m-m,
"I don't know what to say to that,
Till I can see my Uncle Rat." m-m, m-m.

When Uncle Rat came riding home, m-m, m-m,
When Uncle Rat came riding home,
Said he, "Who's been here since I've been gone?"
  m-m, m-m.

"A fine young gentleman has been here," m-m, m-m,
"A fine young gentleman has been here,
Who wants to marry me, it is clear." m-m, m-m.

So Uncle Rat he rode to town, m-m, m-m,
So Uncle Rat he rode to town,
And bought his niece a wedding gown, m-m, m-m.

"Where shall our wedding supper be?" m-m, m-m,
"Where shall our wedding supper be?"
"Down in the trunk of some hollow tree." m-m, m-m.

The first to come was a Bumblebee, m-m, m-m,
The first to come was a Bumblebee,
He strung his fiddle over his knee, m-m, m-m.

The next to come was the Captain Flea, m-m, m-m,
The next to come was the Captain Flea,
He danced a jig with the Bumblebee, m-m, m-m.

The next to come was the big Black Snake, m-m, m-m,
The next to come was the big Black Snake,
And on his head was the wedding cake, m-m. m-m.

The Frog and Mouse they went to France, m-m, m-m,
The Frog and Mouse they went to France,
And this is the story of their romance, m-m, m-m.

Go Tell Aunt Rhody

"GO TELL AUNT RHODY" has a curious history and is a rare example of a piece of composed music beginning at the other end of the musical spectrum from folk music and gradually, by use and familiarity, becoming a genuine folksong. Jean Jacques Rousseau, famous as a philosopher and musician, wrote a one-act opera *Le Devin du Village* (*The Village Soothsayer*) which was performed in 1753 for King Louis XV at Fontainebleau. It met with great success. Some years later it was performed in England and equally well-received. The opera itself has faded from memory, but a melody from Scene 8 has lived on. In 1788 it appeared as a piece for piano, harp or guitar. The composer, Cramer, wrote a set of variations on this theme in 1812. The melody also has appeared in many hymnals under a variety of titles. Meanwhile mothers had begun to make up words for the melody to sing to their children, and so it became a genuine folk song. Perhaps the modern reader may need to be reminded that not so very long ago a goose-feather comforter was an important item in the household and that the drowning of a goose was a very real calamity.

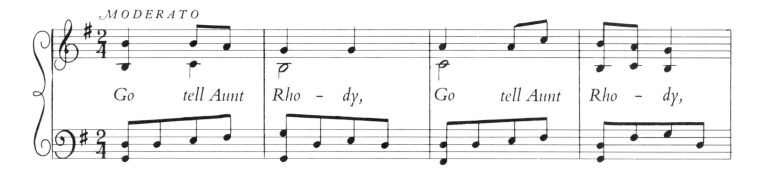

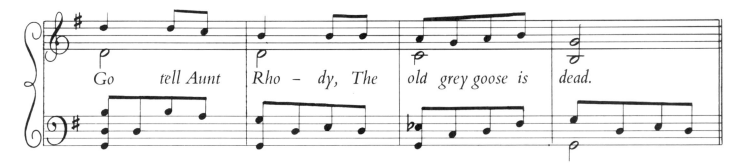

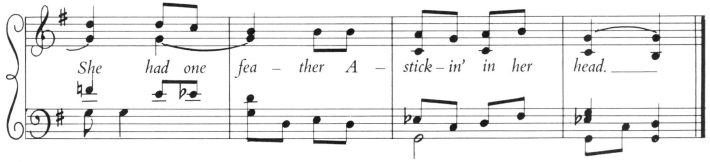

GO TELL AUNT RHODY

Go tell Aunt Rhody,
Go tell Aunt Rhody,
Go tell Aunt Rhody,
The old grey goose is dead.

The one she's been savin',
The one she's been savin',
The one she's been savin',
To make her feather bed.

She drowned in the millpond,
She drowned in the millpond,
She drowned in the millpond,
Standing on her head.

Old gander's weepin',
Old gander's weepin',
Old gander's weepin',
Because his wife is dead.

The goslins are mournin',
The goslins are mournin',
The goslins are mournin',
'Cause their mammy's dead.

She only had one feather,
She only had one feather,
She only had one feather
A-stickin' in her head.

SOUTHERN MICHIGAN

Animal Song

THE "animal song," a familiar type of lullaby which has existed as long as history, is an excellent example of the use of poetry and music as a mnemonic device, a way of learning in this case the names of animals. This shows yet another example of modern "discovery" being, in fact, as old as time. We call the somewhat similar method "sleep learning." This song has an interesting history, since it came to us not in its original form as a lullaby, but as a song sung by men, the heterogeneous work gangs of adventurers, drifters, rovers, and recent immigrants, who opened up southern Michigan. Lacking other forms of entertainment, after a hard day's work, these men often gathered in the evening in the bunk shanty to "chaw tobaccer" and swap yarns and songs. Often the themes centered about some phase of life around them. This song was recorded in 1935 by Marshall Wheatly of Detroit who learned it from his father fifty-odd years earlier.

ANIMAL SONG

Bullfrog, woodchuck, wolverine, goose,
Whippoorwill, chipmunk, jackal, moose.

Mud turtle, whale, glowworm, bat,
Salamander, snail, Maltese cat.

Black squirrel, coon, opossum, wren,
Red squirrel, loon, South Guinea hen.

Reindeer, blacksnake, ibex, nightingale,
Martin, wild drake, crocodile, and quail.

House rat, tosrat, white bear, doe,
Chickadee, peacock, bobolink, and crow.

Eagle, kingeron, sheep, duck, and widgeon,
Conger, armadillo, beaver, seal, pigeon.

Here Take This Lovely Flower

SMALL in number and doomed to disappear almost from the beginning because of their doctrine of strict celibacy, the Shakers were a communitarian religious sect of the utmost devoutness. The American Society of Shakers, founded in 1774, has long since vanished, leaving behind, however, the buildings of their communities and the furniture of utmost simplicity and durability which has served as an inspiration for many modern American designers and artists. It might be wondered how the celibate Shakers found a place for the lullaby in their music. In the first place, all Shakers of all ages strove to be "childlike" in humility, obedience, and simplicity so that they might enter into the Kingdom of Heaven. Moreover, there were many children in the Shaker communities—the children of recent converts, as well as orphans taken in. The songs they sang to them are described as ones received from a heavenly shepherdess. The words of "Here Take This Lovely Flower" are an accurate reflection of the Shakers' "true simplicity" and other-worldly concerns.

HERE TAKE THIS LOVELY FLOWER

Here take this lovely flower
Thy mother sent to thee,
Cull'd from her lovely bower
Of true simplicity.

O place it in thy bosom
And keep it pure and bright,
For in such lovely flowers
The angels take delight.

The Mocking Bird

THE Appalachian Mountains, whose name derives from the Indian tribe of Appalachees, have been a place of great interest to those concerned with folklore and folk music; for here, in the relatively remote uplands and high places, direct descendants of original pioneer stock, English and Scotch-Irish, have lived in near isolation from the rest of the modern world until recent times. Isolation from change has permitted the people of this area to preserve with some continuity their old traditions and even older forms of the English language, even to the idioms and diction of Elizabethan English. Thinly populated and often poor, this region has kept alive its tradition of folk singing as a primary form of solace and entertainment. Here the scholar can trace with some certainty the evolution of traditional British song in a new environment. A traditional lullaby promising rewards to the good child is made regional through the introduction of the southern mockingbird, known and admired for its own tuneful singing, its unusual repertoire of songs, its knack of imitating other bird songs, and as a night singer, a kind of American version of the British nightingale.

THE MOCKING BIRD

Hush up, baby,
Don't say a word,
Papa's gonna buy you
A mockin' bird.

If it don't whistle,
And it don't sing,
Papa's gonna buy you
A diamon' ring.

If that diamon' ring
Turns to brass,
Papa's gonna buy you
A lookin'-glass.

If that lookin'-glass
Just gets broke,
Papa's gonna buy you
A billy-goat.

If that billy-goat
Runs away,
Papa's gonna buy you
Another some day.

Sleep, My Baby, Sleep

IN *Inside U.S.A.* John Gunther wrote, "It would be a rash person who would attempt to define the term 'Pennsylvania Dutch.'" That is an understatement, but some things can be said. First of all they are *not* Dutch. The term is applied freely to early settlers who migrated to Pennsylvania from Bavaria, the Palatinate, and Moravia. There are certain common characteristics which have been recognized. They are an unusually hard-working, farming people, noted for careful cultivation of every available inch of arable land and for extraordinary care of their holdings, equipment, houses, and barns. The result is that their farms are exemplary and among the most beautiful in the United States. They are also noted for the decorative motifs, sometimes called "hex signs," which are painted on many farm buildings, and especially on their fine and sturdy barns. These are reputed to ward off evil spirits. Many of their ways of life are rooted in the Old World. One of the things they brought with them was a love of music and the old songs. "Schloof, Bobbeli, Schloof!" is clearly another version, perhaps more humorous, of the traditional German "Schlaf, Kindlein, Schlaf."

SLEEP, MY BABY, SLEEP

Sleep, my baby, sleep!
Your Daddy's tending the sheep.
Your Mommy's taken the cows away,
Won't come home till break of day.
Sleep, my baby, sleep!

Sleep, my baby, sleep!
Your Daddy's tending the sheep.
Your Mommy's tending the little ones.
Baby sleeps as long as he wants.
Sleep, my baby, sleep!

Sleep, my baby, sleep!
Your Daddy's tending the sheep.
Your Mommy is cooking Schnitz today,
Daddy's keeping the bugs away!
Sleep, my baby, sleep!

Sleep, my baby, sleep!
Your Daddy's tending the sheep.
Your Mommy's gone off on a gossiping flight,
And won't be back till late tonight!
Sleep, my baby, sleep!

SCHLOOF, BOBBELI, SCHLOOF!

Schloof, Bobbeli, Schloof!
Der Daadi hiet die Schoof.
Die Mammi hiet die braune Kieh
Und kummt met heem bis Marriye frieh.
Schloof, Bobbeli, schloof!

Schloof, Bobbeli, schloof!
Der Daadi hiet die Schoof.
Die Mammi hiet die Lemmer,
Noo schlooft des Bobbeli Nock lenger.
Schloof, Bobbeli, schloof!

Schloof, Bobbeli, schloof!
Der Daadi hiet die Schoof.
Die Mammi die kocht Schnitz un Gnebb;
Der Daadi hiet die Keffer weg.
Schloof, Bobbeli, schloof!

Schloof, Bobbeli, schloof!
Der Daadi hiet die Schoof.
Die Mammi iss fatt uff die Blauderyacht
Un sie kummt net heem bis dunkel Nacht.
Schloof, Bobbeli, schloof!

Go Ter Sleep

THERE are many variants and versions of this little "go ter sleep" song, not only in the south but throughout the United States. It is widely popular with both white and Negro families, and Natalie Curtis, who recorded this version, calls it "the song with which the devoted slave-nurse lulled to sleep the children of her master" as well as her own, again indicating the powerful influence of the African mother or *maame* ("mammy" being a variation of the original African word) and coming from a culture which is essentially matriarchal and in which the deity, *Ohemmaa,* is the female creator and Mother of the Universe. Many songs of the Negro reflect his joys and his sorrows and his religious zeal, especially those known as "spirituals" which express deliverance from bondage. There are songs, too, like this one, with a spirit of gentleness that lingers on and on.

Go ter sleep, — ba - by chil' Go ter sleep, ma lit'l' ba - by.

Hush - a bye, don't you cry, Go ter sleep, ma lit'l'

ba - by. When you wake — you will have All de pretty lit'l'

GO TER SLEEP

Go ter sleep, baby chil'
Go ter sleep, ma lit'l' baby.
Hush-a bye, don't you cry,
Go ter sleep, ma lit'l' baby.
When you wake you will have
All de pretty lit'l' horsis.

Black an' blue, sorrel too,
All de pretty lit'l' horsis.
Black an' blue an' sorrel too,
All de pretty lit'l' horsis.
Hush-a bye, don't you cry,
Go ter sleep, ma lit'l' baby, bye.

Gay Creole Gal

LOUISIANA, at one time under Spanish, French, and British rule, has long been known as a cosmopolitan culture, combining elements of all these together with Indian and Negro influences. The word *Creole* originated in the 16th century to denote people of Spanish parentage in the West Indies, but gradually it became widely applied to the languages, forms of Spanish and French spoken by the inhabitants of the New World. For example, the term *French Creole* is applied to the language of Haiti and *English Creole* describes the Jamaican *dialect*. In Louisiana *Creole* refers to the language of the descendants of original French settlers and is distinguished from *Cajun* which is applied to the *patois* of refugees from French Canada (Acadia) whose long journey here was celebrated in Longfellow's "Evangeline." Creole folklore is full of fable and mystery, of talking animals, of spells and enchantments, and that is reflected in "Gay Creole Gal" by the image of talking gourds and alligators and by the menace of the wildcat who stalks in the night.

GAY CREOLE GAL

Gay Creole gal, sweep up that road.
I'll tell him "Yes!" I'll tell him
That gourd can speak,
That gourd can speak.

Gay Creole gal, sweep up that road.
I'll tell him "Yes!" I'll tell him
The alligator can sing,
The alligator can sing.

Gay Creole gal, sweep up that road.
I'll tell him "Yes!" I'll tell him
The wildcat can strangle,
The wildcat can strangle.

GUÉGUÉ SOLIN GAIE

Guégué Solin gaie, balayez chimin-là.
M'a di' li, "Oui!" M'a di' li,
Calebasse, li connain parler,
Calebasse, li connain parler.

Guégué Solin gaie, balayez chimin-là.
M'a di' li, "Oui!" M'a di' li
Cocodri, li connain chanter!
Cocodri, li connain chanter.

Guégué Solin gaie, balayez chimin-là.
M'a di' li, "Oui!" M'a di' li
Pichou, li connain 'trangler,
Pichou, li connain 'trangler.

Hush Little Baby

A MEMBER of the Algonquin family, the Ojibwas are a large tribe in their own right who lived in the regions around Lake Huron and Lake Superior along what is now the border between the United States and Canada. The "naked bear" referred to in the lullaby seems to have been a familiar figure in Indian folklore. The Mohican Indians called him *Ahamagachktiat Mecehqua*, and he was considered to be the largest and most ferocious bear in the world, naked except for one hairy white spot on the back of his neck. Longfellow must have known the legends of this mythical creature and known, as well, of its use by Indian mothers in their lullabys, for he used it in "Hiawatha":

"There the wrinkled old Nokomis
Nursed the little Hiawatha
Rocked him in his linden cradle
Bedded soft in moss and rushes
Safely bound with reindeer sinews
Stilled his fretful wail by saying
"Hush! The naked Bear will hear you.""

HUSH LITTLE BABY

Hush, hush,
Hush little baby,
Go to sleep,
Do not cry,
Or the naked bear
Will eat you.

KAY-GOO-MO-WE-KAYN

Kay-goo-mo-we-kayn
A-bi-no-gees
Wahbshkee muk-wah
Kee-gah-bi-dah-quo-mig
Kah kah-be-shees kos
Kos-kay-be-quay-ne-gen.

Way Off from You

THE Sioux were Indians of the northern plains and lived across an area which now includes the states of Wisconsin, Minnesota, North and South Dakota. Like other Indians of the Great Plains, they were dependent upon hunting for their livelihood, and thus the great herds of buffalo furnished them food, clothing, and hides for their housing. The buffalo had important symbolic significance in their religious life. Survival for the Sioux depended in large part on education of the children for the practical realities of life and the conservation of and respect for tribal traditions. Obedience and respect for elders was primary. The young boys were taught games to prepare them to be hunters and warriors, and they were taught to bear pain without fear. Girls were early instructed in the domestic arts and in herb lore for household as well as medicinal uses. Notice that the mother in this lullaby calls the child to sleep in the form of a signal and a command.

WAY OFF FROM YOU

Way off from you
I am standing.
My blanket I am waving
Mah, mah, mah, mah
Come here to me,
Come here to me.

INK PA TA NA

Ink pa ta
Na waj na-a
Shina chi cho ze
Ma-ma, ma-ma
Le chi ku ya na
Le chi ku ya na

Kawas, Thy Baby Is Crying!

THE Pawnee Tribe is one of the most interesting of the tribes of the Great Plains. They were originally noted for their highly developed religious awareness, an emphasis upon religion which permeated all aspects of their lives, manifesting itself in ritual, ceremony, and complex symbolism, all at times bordering on what we call mysticism. Essentially contemplative, they were among the very first tribes in the whole plains area to make peace with the advancing whites, and as early as 1825 they settled for the reservation life which other tribes resisted for more than half a century. Not that they were entirely passive or without considerable skill as warriors and hunters; for it was with the aid of Pawnee scouts that the West was won. "Kawas, Thy Baby Is Crying" is a ceremonial lullaby, used in conjunction with a "calumet" or peace-pipe ceremony. It is, in fact, a form of prayer sung by the parents in lullaby rhythm to comfort a crying child. "Kawas" is the name given to the brown eagle whose wide-winged, lonely soaring was inevitably a symbol to the Pawnees.

KAWAS, THY BABY IS CRYING!

Kawas, thy baby is crying!
Grieving sore, wailing, and weeping.
Aye, forsooth! wailing and weeping.
Kawas, thy baby is crying.

KAWAS TA WHAKA RATSA WE!

Ho o kawas ta whaka ratsa we!
Kawas ta whaka ratsa we.
Ah hewi! whaka ratsa we,
Kawas ta whaka ratsa we!

Pu'va, Pu'va, Pu'va

IN the Hopi language the name of their tribe derives from and signifies "the peaceful people." They are one of the Pueblo tribes of the southwest, and it may be that physical isolation in the arid region of northeastern Arizona has enabled them to preserve intact much of their culture in spite of the impact of the white man's coming. Song is an integral part of that culture, serving in religious ceremonies, used to cure the sick, to accompany games, work and dances (the Flute and the Snake dances are the best known). Song also served to quiet a restless infant. This lullaby, sung by Hopi mothers, and fathers too, makes the amusing analogy between the custom of carrying infants on their backs and that of the beetles on the trail who sleep on each other's backs.

PU'VA, PU'VA, PU'VA

Pu'va, pu'va, pu'va,
On the trail the beetles
On each others' backs are sleeping.
So on mine, my baby, thou.
Pu'va, pu'va, pu'va.

PU'VA, PU'VA, PU'VA

Pu'va, pu'va, pu'va,
Ho ho ya wu
Shuh po pa ve e.
No i kwi o Kian go
Pu'va, pu'va, pu'va

Central America

Hush, Little One

MEXICO offers a culture in which Indian elements, derived from Aztec and Mayan days, are inseparable from the Spanish. The Yaqui people, an agricultural tribe living along the banks of rivers in the state of Sonora, have managed to preserve much of their Indian heritage, for they are naturally reticent and resisted outside influences longer than any other tribe. Eventually, however, they yielded to the teachings of the Church. In the narrative simplicity of this lullaby— an apple and a hungry mouse together with the notion of a Christian saint as an avenger—there is an echo of an earlier time and the early gods. But the ecclesiastical influence is dominant. The melody is related to the lovely *Prayer to the Virgin* in the language of Nahuatl. This language, also called Aztec, was the ancient language of Mexico. There are, however, extensive remains in existence, largely due to Bernardino de Sahaqún, a 16th-century Spanish monk who wrote down recitations of both prose and verse in Nahuatl, using the Latin alphabet, and thus preserved it for future scholars.

HUSH, LITTLE ONE

Hush, little one,
Why is the baby crying?
Because he lost his apple.
Get up, Saint Cameleon.
A mouse came out from under the floor
Kill him! Kill him! with a stroke of
  your gloved hand.

A LA RORRO NIÑO

A la rorro niño,
Porque llora niño?
Se perdió la manzana.
Levántate San Camaleón
Debajo del pisá salió un ratón
Mátenlo! Mátenlo! de un guantón.

Hush, Hush Child

THE music of Mexico reflects its history and culture very directly. The Mayas and the Aztecs were an advanced culture when Cortez and his horsemen arrived early in the sixteenth century. The music of the Aztecs was an important part of their rituals and ceremonies and, though it has been largely lost to us since the downfall of the Aztec Empire in 1531, it survives in the drums, rattling vessels, and rattling sticks which characterize the percussive rhythms we associate with Mexico. While the words of this gay little melody are richly imaginative, there lurks, too, an acute longing of the mother to return to her native soil.

HUSH, HUSH CHILD	A LA RORRO NIÑO
Hush, hush child.	A la rorro niño
Sleep my child.	A la rorro ro
Now then sleep	Duérmete, mi niño
And I will lull you.	Que lo arrullo yo.
Beautiful little sparrow,	Gorrioncito hermoso,
Beak of coral,	Pico de coral,
I'll bring you a cage	Te traigo una jaula
Made of pure crystal.	De puro cristal.
Beautiful little sparrow,	Gorrioncito hermoso,
Beak of ruby,	Pico de rubí,
I bring a cage	To traigo una jaula
Of gold for you.	De oro para ti.
God Almighty,	Dios Omnipotente,
Take me out of here,	Sácame de aquí,
Take me to my town.	Llévame a mi pueblo
Where I was born.	Donde yo nací.

Go to Sleep, My Little One

GUATEMALA is the most northerly state of Central America. It has a very large Indian population—more than half the people are pure Indian—and it is not surprising that there are many well-preserved Mayan ruins there. The Spanish influence is, of course, predominant, but the bird woven into the pattern of the mother's shawl in the illustration is a descendant of the ancient Quetzal, the sacred bird of the Mayans. The simple and at times primitive life of an almost exclusively agricultural country is reflected in the basic simplicity of the text and music of this lullaby. The ordinary facts of washing and sewing dissolve into a promise of holiday finery on a saint's day. In Guatemala as in other Catholic countries the day of a patron saint is more important and more festive to the child than a birthday. If a Catholic child is not named after some saint, he receives a middle name (sometimes more than one) of that category. He then has a patron saint, who is to look after him. The child pays special reverence to his name-saint all his life and observes his saint's day without fail.

GO TO SLEEP, MY LITTLE ONE

Go to sleep, my little one
For I have things to do.
I have to wash your swaddling clothes
And then sit down to sew.
A little shirt
For you to wear
On your Saint's Day
At early dawn.

DUÉRMETE, NIÑITO

Duérmete, niñito
Que tengo que hacer:
Lavar tus panales,
Sentarme a coser
Una camisita
Que te has de poner
El día de tu santo
Al amanecer.

33

Now Sleep, Little Fellow

EL SALVADOR ("The Savior") is the smallest of the Central American republics and is the only one without an Atlantic seacoast. It is a country of mountains, hills, and upland plains. Nowadays El Salvador is celebrated for its coffee plantations, but in the heyday of the Spanish explorers and *conquistadores* gold was the great lure. And the signs of former affluence are still evident in the elegant gold craftsmanship to be found in the churches, even to the gold necklaces that bedeck the Blessed Virgin. The melody of this lullaby is simple, but there is something of ecclesiastical splendor in the imagery, as of a rich light through a stained glass window.

ANDANTE DOLCEMENTE

Dormite, ni- ni - to, No llores, Chi- qui - to, Vendrán ange - li - tos,

Las sombras do no- che. Rayitos de lu- na Rayitos de plata, Alumbran a mi

ni - ño Que esta en la cu- na. Rayitos del sol, El cielo a- zul

Dejan de dor mir — Y empiezan a vivir. — Dormite, ni-ñi-to,

Con ojos de dia-mantes — Estrellas bri-llantes — Florido el cie-lo.

NOW SLEEP, LITTLE FELLOW

Now sleep, little fellow,
Don't cry, little darling.
The angels are coming,
The shadows of evening.

The rays of the moonlight
Are fine threads of silver,
Will shine on my baby
Asleep in his cradle.

The rays of the sun,
The blue of the sky
Will waken from sleep
And begin to live.

Now sleep, little fellow,
With eyes like diamonds
Atwinkle like starlight
That flowers the heavens.

DORMITE, NIÑITO

Dormite, niñito,
No llores, chiquito,
Vendrán angelitos,
Las sombras de noche.

Rayitos de luna
Rayitos de plata,
Alumbran a mi niño
Que está en la cuna.

Rayitos del sol,
El cielo azul
Dejan de dormir
Y empiezan a vivir.

Dormite, niñito,
Con ojos de diamantes,
Estrellas brillantes
Florido el cielo.

Precious Child

NICARAGUA is a land of lakes and volcanoes. Though it is the largest nation in Central America, it is thinly populated. The percentage of pure-blooded Indians or pure-blooded Spaniards is very small, but the fusion of races is manifest in the unique combination of native Indian ritual elements with Spanish ecclesiastical traditions in present-day Catholic religious rites there. Since music plays such an important role in the ritual of the Catholic Church, the early Fathers did much to

train the converts, even to incorporating some of the ancient musical instruments of the Indians—such as the *maracas* (dried, seed-filled gourds), the *zul* (a primitive flute) and drums of varying sizes—into some of the Church ceremonies. The melodies the Fathers passed on to the people were perforce simple. Curiously, the child's value to the mother expressed in the first stanza of this lullaby is equated with something rare, luxurious and utterly fabulous in that part of the world—the ermine.

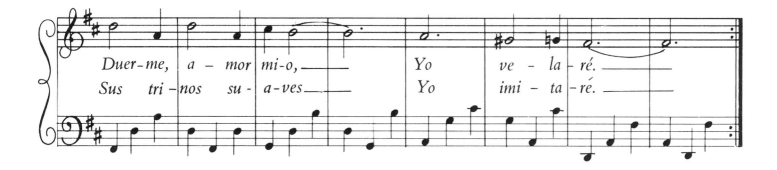

Duer-me, a – mor mi-o,_____ Yo ve - la - ré._____
Sus tri -nos su - a-ves_____ Yo imi - ta -ré._____

PRECIOUS CHILD

Precious child,
More priceless than ermine,
Smiling child,
God of love,

Sleep peacefully;
Sleep while
My humble voice
Is raised in song.

(First refrain)
Sleep, little one,
It is cold today.
Sleep, my love,
I will keep watch.

(Second refrain)
All the birds
Tell you, sleep.
Their sweet chirpings
I will imitate.

NIÑO PRECIOSO

Niño precioso,
Mas que el armiño,
Risueño niño
Dios del amor,

Duerme tranquilo,
Duerme entretanto
Eleva un canto
Mi humilde voz.

(First refrain)
Duerme, chiquitito,
Que hoy hace frío.
Duerme, amor mío,
Yo velaré.

(Second refrain)
Duerme, te dicen
Todas las aves.
Sus trinos suaves
Yo imitaré.

Sleep, Little One

HONDURAS, which means "the depths," got its name directly from Columbus, who sounded the deep coast of the north. It has a long coastline on the Caribbean, and the country is mountainous and covered with forests. Other than the real folk music of the nation and occasional performances by visiting musicians, the only regular musical concerts are offered by military bands. Thus the folk music, as evidenced by this lullaby, is apt to be simple, handed down for generations in the ancient way—by oral tradition—and sung everywhere.

rurrú rrurrú - rrú.   Ar- rú,- ar- ru-rrú,- rú,   Ar - rú; arrur - ru - rú,

SLEEP, LITTLE ONE

Sleep, little one,
I have something to do—
Wash your swaddling clothes
Sit me down to sew.

Sleep, little one,
Pumpkin head,
If you don't sleep,
The coyote will eat you.

Bye-bye, bye,
Bye-bye, bye,
Bye-bye, bye,
Aye aye aye.

DORMITE, NIÑITO

Dormite, niñito,
Que tengo que hacer—
Lavar tus panales;
Sentarme a coser.

Dormite, niñito,
Cabeza de ayote,
Si no te dormis,
Te come el coyote.

Arru, arrurru,
Arru, arrurru,
Arru, arrurru,
Arrurru rrurru rru.

West Indies

Go to Sleep, My Little One

THE music of Cuba, with its distinctive rhythms and melodies, was the first Latin American music to achieve widespread international appreciation, and it has become assimilated and transformed into the idiom of foreign cultures and lands. The culture of Cuba itself is a special one, for the Indian elements, so vital in other Latin nations, have all but disappeared. Essentially Cuba offers a unity of Negro and Spanish characteristics. Discovered by Columbus in 1492, it remained Spanish until 1898, long after its neighbors had achieved independence. In spite of a turbulent and often tragic history, Cuba has produced many distinguished artists, among them renowned composers and musicians. Yet beneath the sophistication of the lively arts lie the deep roots of the Afro-Cuban folklore. This lullaby offers the direct and simple threat of a mysterious cannibal, a dim memory from the dark and far-distant past, if the child doesn't hurry up and go to sleep.

GO TO SLEEP, MY LITTLE ONE

Go to sleep, my little one,
For here comes the black man,
Who eats little children who do not sleep.
Go to sleep, my little one,
Go to sleep, my little one.

DUERMA-SE, MI NIÑITO

Duerma-se, mi niñito,
Que viene el coco,
A comer se los niños que duermen poco.
Duerma-se, mi niñito,
Duerma-se, mi niñito.

Sleep, Mosquitos, Sleep

HAITI is the only French-speaking republic in the Western Hemisphere. It shares the island of Hispaniola with the Dominican Republic. The population is largely Negro, descendents of slaves brought over from Africa in the sixteenth, seventeenth and eighteenth centuries. With them came their religious beliefs, which survive in the cult of the *vodoun*. At the rituals are heard the pulsating rhythms of the drums which accompany the sacred songs and dances. But the more popular songs reflect strong European influences, as, for example, this lullaby with its words in French *patois*. That the mosquito is a fact of life is clear from the song, ironically addressed to the unsleeping mosquito and offered subtly as an articulation of the child's restless discontent.

SLEEP, MOSQUITOS, SLEEP

Sleep, mosquitos, sleep.
Sleep, mosquitos, sleep.
Three hours before dawn
Mosquitos begin to sting.
I know not which position
To shift to!
Sleep, mosquitos, sleep.

DODO, MARINGOUIN DODO

Dodo, maringouin dodo.
Dodo, maringouin dodo.
Trois heu d'ouvant jou'
Bigaill piquer moin.
Moin pas connain position
Moin ve!
Dodo, dodo maringouin.

All Me Rock

LARGEST of the British West Indies, Jamaica has had a fascinating history. It was discovered by Columbus during his second voyage to the New World and captured by the British in 1665, then almost lost by them to hordes of swashbuckling buccaneers and pirates who made Port Royal their home port. In this lul-

laby we have an example of the characteristic dialect, which is found in many forms in the folk songs of Jamaica, together with the equally characteristic assimilated African rhythms. Here the mother contends with the imagination of the child who is roaming "up town" and "down town" in mind, if not in body.

ALL ME ROCK

All me rock, me rock Boysie,
Boysie wouldn't sleep;
All me rock, me rock Boysie,
Boysie wouldn't sleep.

Go up town, go down town,
See Boysie there.

All me rock, me rock Boysie,
Boysie wouldn't sleep;
All me rock, me rock Boysie,
Boysie wouldn't sleep.

Mama Gone A-mountin

THIS LULLABY is widely known and used among the Negroes of Tobago and Trinidad, two of the islands in the West Indies. With both the mother and the father gone, the song is intended to be sung by a nurse or, perhaps, one of the other children acting as a "baby sitter." The *Malatta Man* (mulatto man) will knock down a robin and buy the child a pretty ribbon—a variation on the familiar "daddy's gone ahunting" theme. What is special is the mystery of why the robin will be hung from a treetop. No one knows why this is done. It may be the survival of some lost African ritual whose meaning has long been forgotten.

MAMA GONE A-MOUNTIN

Mama gone a-mountin,
Papa gone a-shootin
Catch one little rabin bird
Heng um up 'pon a tree top

Malata man go knock um dung fo'
Buy me baby ribbin bam,
Buy me baby ribbin bam,
Buy me baby ribbin.

Maracas

Sleep, Sleep, Little One, Sleep

TRINIDAD is the most southerly of the West Indies, lying off the northern coast of South America. It was discovered by Columbus in 1498 and remained a Spanish possession until 1797. Then the British and the French established colonies and the slaves brought from Africa took on both cultures, so evident in the Trinidad folk music. The "steel bands," employing instruments fashioned from steel oil drums and other miscellaneous bits of junk, originated in Trinidad. The calypso songs, sung in a curious kind of English dialect, also had their origin in Trinidad. In this lullaby, the big cat evidently functions much as the bogey man does in the vocabulary of American parents—as a threat to recalcitrant children.

SLEEP, SLEEP, LITTLE ONE, SLEEP

Sleep, sleep, little one, sleep.
Little baby does not wish to sleep.
If my baby will not sleep
The big cat will come and eat you up.

Sleep, sleep, little one, sleep.
Little baby does not want to sleep.
If you do not go to sleep
The big cat will come and eat you up.

DODO PETI' POPO

Dodo peti' popo
Peti' popo pas fait dodo
Si peti' popo pas fait dodo
Macho chat allez mange 'ou.

Dodo peti' popo
Peti' popo pas fait dodo
Si vou' pas dodo peti' popo
Macho chat allez mange 'ou

Oh, My Little Dove

THE first music of the New World Columbus heard was on the island of Santo Domingo, two thirds of which is now occupied by the Dominican Republic; and the first professional musician born in the Western Hemisphere, Cristobal de Llerena, was a native of Santo Domingo. Many distinguished musicians and composers have been natives of this country. For a long time the Spanish tradition in music was the dominating

influence, emanating from the Church and the songs and dances of the people. But the Negro slaves added new life and dimensions, not only to the formal music but to the folklore as well. Though the poetry of "Oh, My Little Dove" clearly belongs to the western folk tradition, it has a sense of fantasy and transformation bordering on the realm of the ancient myths, touching the timeless magic of the fairy tale.

OH, MY LITTLE DOVE

Oh, my little dove   I sat on a tree trunk
Whom I adored,   To see her pass by.
Who grew wings   When she did not pass,
And flew away!   I burst into tears.

She did not eat
Either beans or rice
And she lived
Only on my love.

AY, MI PALOMITA

Ay, mi palomita   Me senté en un tronco
La que yo adoré,   A verla pasar.
Le crecieron alas   Y como no pasaba,
Y voló y se fué!   Me eché a llorar.

Ella no comía
Ni frijolas ni arroz
Y se mantenía
Con solo mi amor

Go to Sleep, My Treasure

PUERTO RICO ("rich port") was discovered by Columbus on his second voyage to the New World in 1493, but it was not actually colonized until 1509 when the celebrated Juan Ponce de Leon became its first governor. The Spaniards found Arawak Indians living there, whom they called Borinquenos after the Indian name for the island. Indians, African slaves, and Spaniards mingled ethnic and cultural strains to form a unique society, marked, at least in those days, by a remarkable absence of any racial prejudice. Although there is a discernible Negro influence in the folk music of Puerto Rico, the centuries of direct contact with Spain, which lasted until the beginning of the 20th century, have kept the Spanish influence predominant. Thus the lullabies of Puerto Rico differ little from those sung by mothers in Andalusia or farther north.

GO TO SLEEP, MY TREASURE

Go to sleep, my treasure,
Go to sleep, my little one,
For the little angels
Are watching you.

Go to sleep, my treasure,
Go to sleep, my baby,
For the night is growing dark.
Go to sleep, my treasure.

DUÉRMASE, RICURA

Duérmase, ricura,
Duérmase, mi niño,
Que los angelitos
Mirándote están.

Duérmase, ricura,
Duérmase, mi niño,
Que la noche obscura.
Duérmase, ricura.

South America

Sleep, Little Child

THIS little song begins where the Bolivian lullaby ended, with a vision of something sweet and good to eat for the child. The amusing turn in the second stanza is addressed to some other listener and thus, ironically, the child is invited to have pity on the singer and go to sleep. The chiefly tropical climate of Venezuela is evoked by the reference to the easily accessible guava, a delicious fruit which the early Spanish explorers were delighted to find growing all the way from Peru to Mexico and now comes to us in a preserve.

SLEEP, LITTLE CHILD

Sleep, little child,
Your mother is not here;
She went to look for guava fruit,
The best ones for you.

If this child does not go to sleep
What a night I shall spend!
I'll spend the night keeping vigil over him,
Singing a lullaby to him.

DUÉRMETE, NIÑO CHIQUITO

Duérmete, niño chiquito,
Que tu madre no está aquí;
Que se fué a buscar guayabas,
Las mejores para ti.

Si este niño no se duerme,
Que noche pasaré yo!
Pasaré la noche en vela,
Cantándole el arrorró.

53

Little Child, Little Child, Sleep a While More

LONG before the arrival of the Spanish *conquistadores* in 1532 the great empire known as the Inca covered all the territory of what is now Peru, Bolivia, Ecuador, and parts of Argentina and Chile. This empire was established by the Quechua-speaking Indians who established a civilization unsurpassed in the Western Hemisphere. Although the Empire crumbled, many of the magnificent Inca structures still stand to remind us of past glories. In Ecuador the Indian descendants of the Incas constitute a majority and the Quechua language is still widely spoken. Their songs and stories come down to us through a long oral tradition. Very little of their folk music shows much Spanish influence. Among their native instruments are the *rondador,* a sort of pan-pipe made of reeds of varying sizes and bound together by fiber, and the *quena,* a reed flute. There is a wide variety of percussive instruments. Ecuador received its name in 1824 from Simon Bolivar, "the Liberator."

LITTLE CHILD, LITTLE CHILD, SLEEP A WHILE MORE

Little child, little child, sleep a while more, little girl.
Sleep a while more, little girl, the goblin will eat you if he finds you awake.
Even in your mother's arms, little girl, the goblin will eat you if he finds you awake.

So, little girl, in your mother's arms, sleep a while more.
You must sleep, so sleep. The goblin will eat you if he finds you awake.
Little girl, sleep a while more. You must sleep.

Sh-sh-sh-sh-sh-sh-sh-sh-. Hush, hush. Sh-sh-sh-sh-.
Sh-sh-sh-sh-sh-sh-sh-sh-. Hush, hush. Sh-sh-sh-sh-.
Sh-sh-sh-sh-sh-sh-sh-sh-. Sleep, you must sleep, sleep.

Little girl, little girl, sleep a while more, sleep.
Little girl, are you in your mother's arms? in your mother's arms?
The goblin will eat you if he finds you awake. Yes, he will eat you,

Little child, little child.
Sh-sh-sh-sh-. Hush, hush.
Sh-sh-sh-sh-sh-sh-sh-sh.
Sh-sh-sh-sh-. Sh-sh-sh-sh-sh-sh-sh-sh-.

WA WA WA WA WAPANDA

Wa wa Wa Wa wapanda, pañuri, mamako
Wapanda pañuri mamako koko shamusha micurani
Mamakunda, mamako, koko shamusha mikurani

Mamako mamakunda wapanda pañuri.
Pañurinda pañuri. Koko shamusha mikurani
Mamako wapanda pañuri pañurinda.

B-b-b-b-b-b-b-a B-b-bu b-b-b-'a
B-b-b-b-b-b-b-a B-b-bu b-b-b-'a
B-b-b-b-b-b-b-i Panuri panurinda panuri

Mamako mamako wapañda pañuri panuri
Mamako mamakunda? mamakunda?
Kuku shamusha mikurani mikurani

Wawako wawako
B-b-b-buB-b-b-bui; B-b-b-b-b-b-bua.
B-b-bua. B-b-b-b-buua.

HUAHUA HUAHUA UN POQUITO MÁS

Huahua huahua un poquito más, duerma mamita,
Un poquito más duerma mamita, viniendo el diablo ha de comer.
Con mamita, mamita, viniendo el diablo ha de comer.

Mamita con mamita un poquito más duerma.
Ha de dormir, duérmase. Viniendo el diablo ha de comer.
Mamita un poquito más duerma, ha de dormir.

B-b-b-b-b-b-b-a B-b-bu b-b-b-'a
B-b-b-b-b-b-b-a B-b-bu b-b-b-'a
B-b-b-b-b-b-b-i duerma, ha de dormir, duerma.

Mamita mamita un poquito más, duerma, duerma.
Mamita, con mamita? con mamita?
Viniendo el diablo ha de comer, ha de comer.

Huahuito huahuito
B-b-b-bu B-b-b-bui; B-b-b-b-b-b-bua.
B-b-bua. B-b-b-b-buua.

Sleep, Little One

COLOMBIA, one of the larger nations of South America, offers yet another example of the successful blending together of diverse cultural and racial strains. Spanish, Negro, and Indian sources have combined to become one. The predominant Spanish influence asserts itself in the melodies of the music, but the rhythms are rooted in the Negro and Indian traditions. Here the child is at first hopefully invited to go to sleep early, surely "before the owl comes"; then in the later verse, ironically, at least "before the rooster crows."

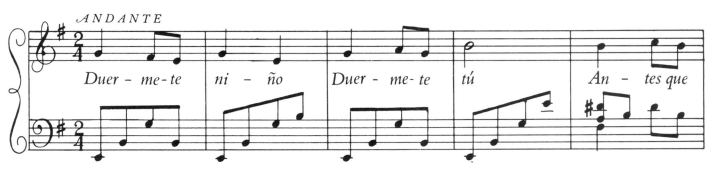

SLEEP, LITTLE ONE

Sleep, little one
Sleep thou, my child,
Before the owl comes.

Sleep, little one,
Sleep thou, my child,
Before the rooster comes.
         Cock-a-doodle-do!

DUÉRMETE, NIÑO

Duérmete, niño
Duérmete tú
Antes que venga el currucutú

Duérmete, niño
Duérmete tú
Antes que venga el guanaguana
         qui-qui-ri-qui

Go to Sleep, My Little One

THIS song is sung to babies who have not learned to walk yet. The mother, holding the child in her lap, accompanies her song with pats, caresses, and gentle body movements. The song is known in many parts of Peru, which has a wide variety of climates, a dry coastline, jungles, and, in the east, the high Andes. Since Peru was the El Dorado of the *conquistadores,* rich in treasure, it drew the energies of the boldest Spanish explorers and the Spanish influence endures strongly. Yet the population is still largely Indian, and through them we have a glimpse of the pre-Columbian world. Peru was once part of that great Incan empire. At the time of the Spanish conquest it had the highest culture in all of South America.

GO TO SLEEP, MY LITTLE ONE

Go to sleep, my little one,
Go to sleep, for God's sake,
For the sake of the hooded mantle
Of St. John the Divine.

Hush, hush-a-bye.
Hush, for God's sake,
For the sake of the hooded mantle
Of St. John the Divine.

DUÉRMETE, NIÑITO

Duérmete, niñito,
Duérmete por Dios,
Por la caperuza
De San Juan de Dios.

A la ruru rita
Duérmete por Dios,
Por la caperuza
De San Juan de Dios.

Little Son, Sleep in the Hammock

THIS is a lullaby of the Paressi Indians who speak the Arawak language. The language is perhaps the most widely distributed Indian tongue-group in South America, transcending national boundaries and even cultures. The Paressi lived in the Mato Grosso region. On the whole, they were a gentle people with a strong leaning toward agriculture. They cultivated large fields of maize, beans and sweet potatoes. The words of this lullaby are simple and repetitive, making the mother even more drowsy than the child. While the melody is primitive, it is quite remarkable in its chromatic range and sequences.

Paressi Indian

LITTLE SON, SLEEP IN THE HAMMOCK

Little son, sleep in the hammock;
Little son, sleep in the hammock.

Little son, sleep in the hammock;
Little son, sleep in the hammock.

Will my little boy sleep in the hammock?
Will my little boy sleep in the hammock?

Will my little boy sleep in the. hammock?
Little son, sleep in the hammock.

Sleep—hammock. Ah ——— .

Ê-NÁ MÔKÔCÊ CÊMÁKÁ

Ê-ná môkôcê cêmáká
Ê-ná môkôcê cêmáká

Ê-ná môkôcê cêmáká
Ê-ná môkôcê cêmáká

U-i-kô môkôcê cêmáká
U-i-kô môkôcê cêmáká

U-i-kô môkôcê cêmáká
Ê-ná môkôcê cêmáká

Cê-má-ká má—ká——á

Boo! Maramba

BRAZIL, which covers nearly half of South America, is unique in being the only Portuguese-speaking country in the Western Hemisphere. Her Portuguese heritage survives in a distinct culture which has managed to assimilate Celtic, Nordic and Moorish strains, together with the folkways of the Negro and the Indian. All races and all creeds are Brazilian. There is much warmth and vitality in Brazilian folk music. This lullaby is as well known in Europe as it is in the United States and in Brazil. The sound of the armadillo scratching and the image of the spider serve to accompany this charming melody and ease the child to sleep.

Tu-tu Marambá, não venhas mais cá Que o pae do menino, te manda matá; Tu-

tú marambá, não venhas mais cá, Que o pae do meni - no, te man - da mata.

Dorm'engracadinho, peque - nino da mamãe, Qu'elle é bonitinho o fil hinho da mamãe! A-

ra- nha Tata- nha, A - ra-nha Tati - nha, Ta-tu and' arranhan-do a tu - a ca-si-nha, A-

ra - nha -nha, A - ra - nha Tati - nha, Ta-tu é que arra - nha a tu - a casi - nha.

BOO! MARAMBA   TUTU MARAMBÁ

Boo! Maramba, don't come here any more,   Tutu Marambá, não venhas mais cá
For the little boy's father orders you to be killed. Que o pae do menino, te manda matá;
Boo! Maramba, don't come here any more,   Tutu Marambá, não venhas mais cá,
For the little boy's father orders you to be killed. Que o pae do menino, te manda matá.
Sleep, darling, Mother's little one,   Dorm'engraçadinho, pequenino da mamae,
How handsome is Mother's little son!   Qu'elle é bonitinho o filhinho da mamae!
Spider Tatanha, Spider Tatinha,   Aranha Tatanha, Aranha Tatinha,
Armadillo is going around scratching your little house. Tatu and' arranhando a tua casinha,
Spider Tatinha, Spider Tatinha,   Aranha Tatanha, Aranha Tatinha,
It's armadillo who is scratching your little house. Tatu e que arranha a tua casinha.
So hush-a-by, behind that heap,   Su, su, su, su, atraz do murundu,
Eat up this little fellow with beans and manioc flour. Comer este menino com feijão e angu!
Boo! Maramba, don't come here any more,   Tutu Marambá, não venhas mais cá,
For the little boy's father orders you to be killed. Que o pae do menino te manda matá.
Boo! Maramba, don't come here any more,   Tutu Marambá, não venhas mais cá,
For the little boy's father orders you to be killed. Que o pae do menino te manda matá.

Our Lady Saint Anne

IN the high, landlocked country of Bolivia, named for the patriot Simon Bolivar, the descendants of the Incas and the *conquistadores* live among the towering peaks of the Andes. The air is thin, and the landscape is bleak, cloudy, and harshly beautiful. This lullaby is Spanish and probably comes from the valley, for it lacks the melancholy austerity associated with the melodies of the mountain people. The child, on the edge of sleep, overhears a gentle prayer to Saint Anne which offers the bright vision of a ripe, red apple to dream on.

OUR LADY SAINT ANNE	SEÑORA SANTA ANA
Our Lady Saint Anne,	Señora Santa Ana,
Why is baby crying?	Porque llora niño
For a nice red apple,	Por una manzana
Hidden somewhere, it's lying.	Que se le ha perdido.
Tell him not to cry,	Decidle que no llore
Because I have two,	Que yo tengo dos;
One for the baby	Una para el niño
And another one for you.	Y otra para vos!

Sleep, My Baby

URUGUAY, though it is larger than England, is the smallest country in South America. Her temperate and flat land is especially suited to farming and ranching. Her coastline, opening out to the sea, has exposed her to many foreign influences, but the Spanish is the almost completely dominant one. The culture of the native Indian has virtually vanished. The folk music is akin to that of neighboring Argentina. This lullaby uses the device of loving flattery to lull the infant, while blaming that rogue sleep itself for keeping the child awake.

SLEEP, MY BABY

Sleep, my little one,
Sleep, my sunshine.
Sleep, thou piece
Of my heart.

This beautiful child
Wants sleep,
But the mischievous sleep
Does not want to come.

ARRORRO, NIÑO

Arrorro, mi niño,
Arrorro, mi sol,
Arrorro, pedazo
De mi corazón.

Este niño lindo
Se quiere dormir
Y el pícaro sueño
No quiere venir.

Sleep, Blessed Babe

"BY the help of God and the power of music" the early Jesuit missionaries exercised an enormous influence on the natives of Chile. They used Latin, the international language of the Church, not only for the business of records and reports, but also in daily life and in their songs. So it is not strange that the descendants of the original Araucanian Indians should sing a lullaby in medieval Latin. As a matter of fact, these Latin lines were first published in the *London Courier* in 1811 with this introduction by Samuel Taylor Coleridge. "About thirteen years or more, travelling through the middle of Germany, I saw a little print of the Virgin and Child in a small public house of a Catholic village, with the following beautiful Latin lines under it, which I transcribed." Evidently these Latin lines were also known to the Jesuit fathers who came to Chile on their missions. The melody to which these Latin lines were set is very definitely Spanish.

Dormi, Je-su,— blan-du-le! —— Blande ve-ni, somnu-le. ——

Blande ve-ni, somnu-le. ——

SLEEP, BLESSED BABE

Sleep, blessed babe, and mother will smile,
Happily guarding her treasure the while.
If thou art wakeful, mother will weep,
Her song and her spindle silent will keep.

Sleep, blessed babe, let slumber come softly,
Let slumber come gently, let slumber come sweetly.
Sleep blessed babe, let slumber come softly,
Let slumber come gently, let slumber come sweetly.

DORMI, JESU

Dormi, Jesu, mater ridet,
Quae tam dulcem somnum videt.
Si no dormis, mater plorat,
Inter fila cantans orat.

Dormi, Jesu, blandule!
Blande veni, somnule.
Dormi, Jesu, blandule
Blande veni, somnule

Arrorro, My Baby

ARGENTINA is the largest Spanish-speaking nation in the hemisphere. It is also one of the most richly endowed with natural resources and one of the most prosperous, as the name, derived from the Latin for "silver," implies. One of the special characteristics of Argentine folkways is the celebrated figure of the *gaucho*, the cowboy who rides herds across the vast ranch lands. The Spanish introduced cattle to the hemisphere at the urging of Columbus. As soon as the first years of conquest were over, the Church entered vigorously into its mission of teaching and conversion, soon branching out to every big and little settlement. Realizing that music was a language the natives understood, the Church fathers went about learning the songs of the natives and in turn taught them many a hymn. The results and the strong effects of their teachings can be seen in the example of this lullaby, which takes on the imagery of the Lord, His angels, and the heavens.

ANDANTE SOSTENUTO

Ar - ror - ro, mi ni - ño, Ar - ror - ro, mi sol,

Ar - ror - ro, pe - da - zo De mi co - ra - zon.

Es - te ni - ño lin - do Se quiere dor - mir Y

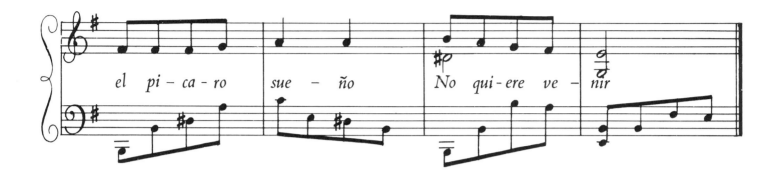

el pi – ca – ro sue – ño No qui – ere ve – nir

ARRORRO, MY BABY

Arrorro, my baby,
Arrorro, my sunshine
Arrorro, little bit
Of my heart.

This beautiful baby
Wants to sleep,
But the mischievous sleep
Does not want to come.

This beautiful baby
Wants to sleep.
He closes his eyes
And opens them again.

An angel from heaven
Sent by the Lord
Will watch over your dreams,
Angel of my love.

ARRORRO, MI NIÑO

Arrorro, mi niño,
Arrorro, mi sol,
Arrorro, pedazo
De mi corazón.

Este niño lindo
Se quiere dormir
Y el pícaro sueño
No quiere venir.

Este niño lindo
Se quiere dormir
Cierra los ojitos
Y los vuelve a abrir.

Un ángel del cielo
Mandado por Dios
Velará tu sueño,
Angel de mi amor.

Scandinavia

Ammassalik Eskimo

How Charming He Is That Little Pet There!

IN Arctic Greenland there has been enough mixture of the Danish and Eskimo strains so that the people are known as neither, but rather as Greenlanders. Actually the Vikings were in Wineland, as they called it then, for some five centuries before the migratory Ammassalik Eskimos arrived and settled there. The Eskimos are a hardy people, able to endure the bleak landscape and the cold, living chiefly, as of old, by hunting and fishing. Although the folk music for adults allows for religious sentiments and often for mature resentment of the difficulties of life, the children's songs are almost uniformly idyllic. It is an Eskimo tradition to "spoil" the young with lavish love and constant attention. Some of this adulation is evident in this Greenland lullaby.

HOW CHARMING HE IS THAT LITTLE PET THERE!

How charming he is that little pet there!
How charming he is—!
How amazing he is, the dear little creature!

How bland he is and gentle, the great
    little one there!
How bland he is and gentle—
How amazing he is, the dear little creature!

How sound he looks and vigorous, the great
    little thing there!
How sound he looks and vigorous!
How amazing he is, the dear little creature!

ER-KWEE-NANG-WAR-TEEWAH-REE-NAH

er-kwee-nang-war-teewah-ree-nah ah yah a-yah-ah
    yah-ah-yah
ay-er-kwee-nah-yah a-yah-ah kah-kang-oo-ar-tee-war

sah-eemah-nang-war-teewah-ree-nah ah yah a-yah-ah
    yah-ah-yah
sah-mah-nah yah ah-yah yah kah-kang war-tee wah

tah-oh-tee-nang-war-teewah-ree-nah ah yah a-yah-ah
    yah-ah-yah
tah-oh-tee-nah yah ah-yah yah kah-kang war-tee-wah

eˑrqinaɔˑuartiwarína ajaˑja

eˑrqinaɔˑuartiwarína ajaˑja   saˑⁱmanaɔuartiwar̈ína ajaˑja   taˑᵒtinaˑɔˑuartiwarína ajaˑja
eˑrqinaˑja ajaˑja   saˑmanaˑja ajaˑja   taˑᵒtinaˑja ajaˑja
kakaɔˑuartiwar   kakaɔˑuartiwar   kakaɔˑuartiwar

Sleep, My Darling Baby
Sleep

THE ICELANDERS are the direct descendants of the early Viking settlers, and their language has changed very little since it was a dialect of Old Norse. The country is bleak and treeless, largely composed of volcanic rock and a huge central ice cap. Yet there is a singular phenomenon in the natural hot springs which provide water, hot enough for many domestic purposes. Iceland has always tested the mettle of its in-habitants. Only scattered areas along the coasts are farmed or inhabited. The lost world of the ancient Norse sagas is evoked in this lullaby by the reference to the protection of hidden treasures, a common motif in Scandinavian myth. The *Althing,* or General Assembly, of Iceland is the oldest democratic legislative body in the world today. As early as 930 a constitution provided for this kind of legislative representation.

SLEEP, MY DARLING BABY SLEEP

Sleep, my darling baby sleep;
Rain is gently falling.
Mother will thy treasures keep,
Hidden where the shadows creep.
Hush thee my baby! Night for rest is calling.

SOFOU ÚNGA ÁSTIN MÍN

Sofou únga ástin mín;
Úti regnið groetur.
Mamma geymir gullin pín,
Gamla leggi' og völuskrín.
Við skulum ekki vaka' um dimmar noetur.

Sleep Gently Now My Little Friend

MANY folksongs are migratory, and wherever they wander they make themselves at home. This lullaby is an excellent example. It was first heard in France as "Ah! Vous Dirai-je Maman"; Mozart later wrote a set of nine variations around the original French version. In Germany, as nursery songs, the melody was set to "Alle meine Entchen" and "Häslein in der Grube." It reappeared in England as the setting for "Baa, Baa, Black Sleep." When it reached Norway, the tune was only slightly modified. Once again it returned to France where it was used by Adolphe Charles Adams in his opera *Le Toreador* (1849). The tune then crossed the Atlantic to America where it was used to learn the letters of the alphabet. We also know it as "Twinkle, Twinkle, Little Star." It traveled eastward to Czechoslovakia and then on to Hungary where within recent times Ernest von Dohnyani used it in a set of variations for piano and orchestra. Only yesterday youngsters in America used this melody to sing "I'm a little teapot short and stout, tip me over and pour me out."

SLEEP GENTLY NOW MY LITTLE FRIEND

Sleep gently now my little friend.
Mama will come back again.
Papa will go over the high bridge
To buy my little Thea new shoes,
New shoes with buckles, too.
So sleep, my Thea, sleep well,
My dear.

SOV NÅ SØTT MIN LILLE VENN

Sov nå søtt min lille venn,
Mamma kommer skart ig-jen.
Pappa går på heye bro,
Kjoper thea nye sko,
Nye sko med spenner på
Så sover hun thea så
Lenge en-da.

Rock, Rock the Child

NORWEGIAN Vikings gave this cluster of eighteen islands its name, calling them For-eyar or Sheep Islands. Though the islands are now part of Denmark, the early Norse influence persists in the Faroese language, still spoken by the islanders. Chiefly fishermen, the Faroe islanders handle their boats in the rough and treacherous north Atlantic with almost unbelievable skill.

The sea is the true cradle song for every Faroese and all too often his requiem as well. In this relative isolation, medieval ballads and folksongs and the folk traditions have remained with exceptional purity. The Faroese are known for their dancing, which is accompanied only by the voice, part of an oral tradition which has been kept intact even in the modern world of today.

ANDANTINO

Ru – ra, ru – ra bar – niò Grytan stendur i jar – – ni,

Mamman situr og tres – kir korn, Pá – pin blásir i fa – gurt horn.

Sis – tur sey – mar klae – òir up – pá bar – – niò. Vil ik – ki bar – niò

ti - - ga,   *Takum legg,*   *slá i vegg,*   *So skal barnið*   ti - - ga.

ROCK, ROCK THE CHILD

Rock, rock the child,
The pot is on the iron,
Mother is sitting and grinding grain,
Father blows a pretty horn.
Sister sews clothes for the child.
If the child will not be quiet,
Take a table leg, pound it on the wall,
Then the child will be quiet.

RURA, RURA BARNIÐ

Rura, rura barnið
Grýtan stendur i jarni,
Mamman situr og treskir korn,
Pápin blásir i fagurt horn.
Sistur seymar klædir uppá barnið.
Vil ikki barnið tiga,
Takum legg, slá i vegg,
So skal barnið tiga.

RŌO'RŬ, RŌO'RŬ BÄTN'NĒ

Rōo'rŭ, rōo'rŭ bätn'nē,
Grōo ē'tän stēn'tŏŏr ōo'ē yät'nē,
Mäm'ən sēe'tŏŏr ō'ə trĕs'chər kätn,
Pä'pən blä'sər, ōo'ē fĕ'vōort hätn.
Sēs'tŭr sā'mär klĕ'yēr ōop'pōo ə
     bät'nē.
Vēl ĭt'chə bät'nē tē'yə
Tĕk ōom lĕk, slō'ä ōo'e vĕk,
Sō'ä skăl bät'nē tē'yä.

Tu... Tu! Aren't You Coming?

AS a nation Sweden began with the union of the Goths and the Svears in the 9th century. Within the context of a highly modern society the Swedes preserve much of their ancient heritage in native costumes and in festivals like Christmas and Midsummer's Eve which are celebrated in a unique manner. Their folklore is full of interesting myths and characters, including the especially engaging *Tomten*, a friendly household spirit in the farm lands who is said to be visible only on Christmas Eve, like our Santa Claus. The Christmas season is ushered in with a Festival of Lights on Saint Lucia Day —December 13th. A young girl attired in white with a crown of evergreens studded with flickering candles brings morning coffee and Lucia buns to each member of the family. The Christmas festivities continue for a month, brightening the long, dark days of winter.

TU...TU! AREN'T YOU COMING?

Shepherd calls: "Tu...Tu! Aren't you coming?
Shepherdess
  answers: "No, can't come yet,
          Must drive the cattle to pasture,
          Must work in the fields yet."

    Shepherd: "Suselisu! Aren't you coming yet?"
Shepherdess: "No, no...can't.
          Must pour the milk into the horn
          For our little one to drink."

TU LU! KOMMER DU AN?

Gossen: "Tu lu! Kommer du an?"
Kullan: "Nej, nej, jag kommer ej,
        Har förfall och far inte gà vall,
        Jag gár pa gardet och harvar."

Gossen: Tullerilull! Kommer du än?
Kullan: "Nej, nej, inte än,
        Mjölka kon och slá i horn,
        Och ge den lille att dricka!"

Shepherd: "Suselisu! Isn't he asleep yet?"   Gossen: "Tullerilull! Sover han än?"
Shepherdess: "Yes, yes...Now I'm here.   Kullan: "Ja, ja, gör han sa!
      The birch tree is swinging the   Björken bláser och lullan gár,
      cradle in the wind,   Den lille han sover i skogen."
      And soon our little one will be
      asleep in the woods."

DENMARK

Sleep, My Little One

DENMARK, not including Greenland and the Faroe Islands, which are also Danish, consists of the Jutland Peninsula and more than 500 surrounding islands. Though small in area and in population (4.5 million) Denmark is widely known throughout the world for its dairy products, its craftsmanship, its progressive government and celebrated hospitality. Hans Christian Andersen, had something to do with preserving this lullaby for posterity. He wrote the forword for the collection, *Bernenes Musik* (1850), from which it is taken.

SLEEP, MY LITTLE ONE

Lullaby, my baby,
Had I only now such four—
Four-and-twenty in a row—
Then should all the cradles go
Lullaby, my baby.
Lullaby, my baby.

VISSELULLE, MIN LIRE

Visselulle, min Lire,
Havde jeg suadanne fire
Fire-og-tyve i hver en Vraa
Saa skulde alle vore Vugger gaa,
Visselulle, min Lire!
Visselulle, min Lire!

77

British Isles

Bye Baby Bunting

IN Old English cradle songs were called *Byssinge,* the prefix *by* meaning slumber. This joyous little song is as old as English nursery rhymes. English mothers have sung it to their babies and it is familiar wherever the English language is spoken. The melody has come down through the years unchanged. As in the case of lullabies of many other lands, the promise of a reward for good behavior is offered to the child. Here the reward is a soft rabbit skin and the good behavior is, of course, sleep. In current English the word "bunting" may refer to a kind of bird or to a soft, thick cloth. Or it may often be simply a term of endearment.

BYE BABY BUNTING

Bye baby bunting,   Gone to get a rabbit skin
Daddy's gone a-hunting.   To wrap his baby bunting in.

Little Red Bird of the Black Turf

THE Manx people have an essentially Gaelic culture, an imprint left by early Irish and Scottish sea traffic with the small Isle of Man. Since the year 1290, however, the Manx have been under the English flag; and in the centuries which have followed, English has gradually replaced the Manx tongue, known only to a few nowadays. But vigorous efforts are now being made to revive it. The ancient lore and legend which survive on the island as well as the native music have been retained largely through the power of oral tradition, and it was not until 1820 that any of the Manx music actually appeared in print.

ANDANTE

Ushag veg ruy ny moanee doo, Moanee doo, moanee doo,

Ushag veg ruy ny moanee doo, C'raad chaddil oo riyr 'syn oie?____ Nagh

chaddil mish riyr er baare y crouw, Baare y crouw, baare y crouw, Lesh

Manx, U.K.

fli– ag hey | tuittym | er dagh | cheu, As | ogh! my | chadley cha | treih!____

LITTLE RED BIRD OF THE BLACK TURF

Little red bird of the black turf
Black turf, black turf
Little red bird of the black turf,
Where did you sleep last night?
Did I not sleep on top of a twig
Top of a twig, top of a twig
With the rain falling on each side
And Oh! my sleep was so poor.

Little red bird of the black turf
Black turf, black turf
Little red bird of the black turf
Where did you sleep last night?
Did I not sleep on top of the thorns
Top of the thorns, top of the thorns
And when the wind blew it bore me up
And Oh! my sleep was so poor.

Little red bird of the black turf
Black turf, black turf
Little red bird of the black turf
Where did you sleep last night?
Did I not sleep on top of a wave
Top of a wave, top of a wave
As many men's sons slept before me
And Oh! my sleep was so poor.

Little red bird of the black turf
Black turf, black turf
Little red bird of the black turf
Where did you sleep last night?
Oh! I slept last night between two leaves
Between two leaves, between two leaves
As slept the child on his mother's breast
An Oh! my sleep was so calm.

USHAG VEG RUY NY MOANEE DOO

Ushag veg ruy ny moanee doo,
Moanee doo, moanee doo,
Ushag veg ruy ny moanee doo,
C'raad chaddil oo riyr 'syn oie?
Nagh chaddil mish riyr er baare y crouw,
Baare y crouw, baare y crouw,
Lesh fliag hey tuittym er dagh cheu,
As ogh! my chadley cha treih!

Ushag veg ruy ny moanee doo,
Moanee doo, moanee doo,
Ushag veg ruy ny moanee doo,
C'raad chaddil oo riyr 'syn oie?
Nagh chaddil mish riyr er baare ny dress,
Baare ny dress, baare ny dress,
Tra va'n gheay sheidey v'eh gymmyrkey lhee,
As ogh! my chadley cha treih!

Ushag veg ruy ny moanee doo,
Moanee doo, moanee doo,
Ushag veg ruy ny moanee doo,
C'raad chaddil oo riyr 'syn oie?
Nagh chaddil mish riyr er baare y tonn,
Baare y tonn, baare y tonn,
Myr shimmey mac dooinney cadley roym,
As ogh! my chadley cha treih!

Ushag veg ruy ny moanee doo,
Moanee doo, moanee doo,
Ushag vey ruy ny moanee doo,
C'raad chaddil oo riyr 'syn oie?
O chaddil mish riyr eddyr daa ghuillag,
Eddyr daa ghuillag, eddyr daa ghuillag,
Myr cadley ny oikan er keeagh y vumming,
As O! my chadley cha kiune!

Sleep, O Babe

DURING long winter evenings, before the turf fire, family and friends often gather around to listen to the long, tall tales of the countryside. These tales are noted for their humor and their imagination. Sometimes they tell about phantoms and ghosts, of fairies, both benign and mischievous, who live in knolls, mounds, and in rocky places. The Irish gift of imagery is lavished on the songs they sing to their babies. Fanciful, rich with figures out of old myths and legends, the poetry is most moving. The music has a haunting quality. This lullaby was taken down many years ago by Patrick MacAodha O'Neill. The original words were lost and came to us in English; in due time, they were retranslated into Gaelic, still spoken in Western Ireland.

SLEEP, O BABE

Sleep, O babe, for the red bee
  hums
The silent twilight's fall.
Eeval from the Gray Rock comes
To wrap the world in thrall.

A lyan van o, my child, my joy,
My love and heart's desire.
The crickets sing you lullaby
Beside the dying fire.

Dusk is drawn, and the Green
  Man's thorn
Is wreathed in rings of fog;
Sheevra sails his boat till morn
Upon the starry bog.

A lyan van o, the paly moon
Hath brimm'd her cusp in dew
And weeps to hear the sad sleep-
  tune,
I sing, O love, to you . . .

CUDDIL A LANV

Cuddil a lanv, taw un veacog vuee
Eg cronawn un chlap-holais cheuen
Shu chuing aoivill na Karaige Layhe
Chun un tueel du chur chun sooin.

A lanvawn oh, mu roon, mu hoh
Mu ghraw augus dooil mu chruee
Du hoontree voul, eg na grager a
  gawawil
Augus un tineh ag dull inague.

Duirke anish, iss sceach 'n Ir Glash
Oss ryarc lu caipeenee keoighe
Showla a vaudeen, ben Shiavra gu
  madin
Ar un burtach, rayltach beoga.

A lanvawn oh, taw un Gealoch vawn
Lawn fah vueel leh droocht,
Ogus gullan go bug, un soon fort do
  chlus
A gauwaim muh grawdeen guit.

CODAIL A LEANB

Codail a leanb, tá'n beacóg buide
Ag crónán an clap foluir ciuin
Seo cugainn Aoibeall na Carraige
  léite
Cun an traogail do cur cun ruain.

A leanbáin Ó, mo rún, mo róg,
mo gráb 'gur dúil mo croibe.
Do ruantraige mall, ag na
  screagair a' gaball
'Gur an teine ag dul i n-éag.

Doirce anoir, ir rceac 'n fir glair
Ar rabarc le caipíní ceoige.
'Seolab a báioín, béib Siabra
  go maivin,
Ar an bportac, réaltac, beobá.

A leanbáin Ó, tá an gealac bán,
Lán fá maoil le drúct,
'Gur golann go bos, an ruan-port
  do clor,
A gabaim mo gráióín óuit.

Lullaby, My Pretty One

THE Welsh have long been famous for their music, particularly their vocal music. More than a thousand years ago the Welsh king, Howel Dha, gave his royal blessing to the most musically gifted of his people by establishing an hereditary order of bards. The bards of Wales were not only poets, but minstrels as well, celebrating legend and history in verse and song. This ancient tradition has been carried forward to the pres-

ent time in the celebrated *Eisteddfod* (bardic assembly) held annually in some towns in Wales. One does not soon forget the rich, warm quality of the singing of a Welsh choir, and the undercurrent of emotion in their voices. Dr. J. Lloyd Williams, Professor of Botany as well as a musician, notated this lullaby when it was sung by one R. Jones of Trefriw. It is one of the many melodies which Dr. Williams saved from possible oblivion.

LULLABY, MY PRETTY ONE

Lullaby, my pretty one,
Gone the day and set the sun.
Lullaby, my pretty one,
And sleep until the morning,
And sleep until the morning.

Little one, now take thy rest
Like the birdie in its nest.
Little one, now take thy rest
And sleep until the morning
And sleep until the morning.

Lullaby, my dearest one,
Sleep for now thy play is done,
Lullaby my dearest one,
And sleep until the morning
And sleep until the morning.

CYSGA DI, FY MHLENTYN TLWS

Cysga di, fy mhlentyn tlws,
Wedi cau a chloi y drws;
Hwian hwi fy mhlentyn tlws,
Cei gysgu tan y bore
Cei gysgu tan y bore.

Cysga dy fy mychan glan
Cysgu mae yr adar man
Hwian hwi fy mychan glan
Cei gysgu tan y bore
Cei gysgu tan y bore,

Hwian hwi fy nghariad i
Ceffyl bach yn d'ymyl di;
Hwian hwi fy nghariad i,
Cei gysgu tan y bore
Cei gysgu tan y bore.

Sleep On Till Dawn

FROM the proud clans of the Scottish Highlands comes this traditional melody. Only the air "Cadul gu lo" (Sleep on till dawn) and not the original Scottish verses were used when a dramatization of Sir Walter Scott's *Guy Mannering* was presented. For this, Sir Walter Scott composed the verses "Lullaby of an Infant Chief" as they are presented here. The history of the Highlands and the interminable wars by which the clans were able to preserve their hard-won independence against overwhelming odds are evoked in this first song for an infant. The dream is of the trumpet and the ideal is manhood. The lines of this lullaby are familiar to us as a nursery rhyme. They are but a curtailed version of Sir Walter Scott's verses.

SLEEP ON TILL DAWN

O Ho ro, i ri ri, sleep on till dawn
O ho ro, i ri ri, sleep on till dawn

O hush thee my babie,
Thy sire was a knight,
Thy mother a ladye,
Both gentle and bright.

O Ho ro, i ri ri, sleep on till dawn
O ho ro, i ri ri, sleep on till dawn

O hush thee my babie,
The time soon will come
When thy sleep shall be broken
By trumpet and drum.

O ho ro, i ri ri, sleep on till dawn
O ho ro, i ri ri, sleep on till dawn

Then hush thee my darling,
Take rest while you may,
For strife comes with manhood,
And waking with day.

O ho ro, i ri ri, sleep on till dawn
O ho ro, i ri ri, sleep on till dawn

LULLABY OF AN INFANT CHIEF

O ho ro, i ri ri, cadul gu lo,
O ho ro, i ri ri, cadul gu lo.

O, hush thee, my babie, thy sire was a knight,
Thy mother a lady both lovely and bright;
The woods and the glens, from the towers which we
    see,
They all are belonging, dear babie, to thee.

O ho ro, i ri ri, cadul gu lo,
O ho ro, i ri ri, cadul gu lo,

O, fear not the bugle, though loudly it blows,
It calls but the warders that guard thy repose;
Their bows would be bonded, their blades would be
    red,
Ere the step of a foeman draws near to thy bed.

O ho ro, i ri ri, cadul gu lo,
O ho ro, i ri ri, cadul gu lo,

O, hush thee, my babie, the time soon will come,
When thy sleep shall be broken by trumpet and drum;
Then hush thee, my darling, take rest while you may,
For strife comes with manhood and wakening with
    day.

O ho ro, i ri ri, cadul gu lo,
O ho ro, i ri ri, cadul gu lo.

Sleep, Sleep, My Child

SCOTLAND, exposed on three sides to the winds and waves of the Atlantic and the North Sea, has a rich storehouse of folk songs. There are ballads which relate historical events and recount legendary lore, and there are many songs which mingle scenes of adventure with domestic life. Naturally the sea-going men developed songs to ease their toil and their loneliness. The women left at home sang of their loneliness and anxiety as well. "Sleep, Sleep, My Child" combines a moving melody with a prayer for a sailor's safe return from the sea.

SLEEP, SLEEP, MY CHILD

Sleep, sleep, my child.
Sleep, sleep, my child,
And may, oh may the men return
Who have gone across the seas!

BA-BA, MO LEANABH

Ba-ba, mo leanabh, ba-ba, ba-ba.
Ba-ba, mo leanabh, ba-ba, ba-ba.
Faill i faill o, faill eill oroho
Gu'n till na fearaibh a dh'fhalbh thar sail.

West Europe

Sleep, My Precious Chick

THE Walloons live in the Belgian provinces of Hainault, Naumur, and Liège, and in Luxembourg. They speak a language closely related to French which, with official status as one of the two languages of Belgium, distinguishes them from their Dutch-speaking, Flemish neighbors. Belgium's place in music history is an important one and Wallonia contributed much to it, especially in the nineteenth century. In Liège, César Franck was born and from the immediate vicinity came a long line of string virtuosi and music historians.

SLEEP, MY PRECIOUS CHICK

Sleep, my precious chick,
Sleep, my little chick.
Your father has gone to the fair.
He will bring you many goodies.
Sleep,....

Sleep, my precious chick,
Sleep, my little chick.
Your mother has gone to church.
When she'll return, you'll have some onion soup.
Sleep,....

NÂNEZ, BINAMÊYE POYÈTE

Nânez, binamêye poyète,
Nânez, binamé poyon.
Y-a s'papa qu'èst-evôye al fièsse
Rapwètrè dès bons crostilyons.
Nânez,....

Nânez, binamêye poyète,
Nânez, binamé poyon.
Y-a s'mame qu'èst-evôye è pwèce,
Rapwètre dèl sope a lognon.
Nânez,....

Toutouig

THE BRETONS have deep roots in a Celtic past and have kept a distinct culture and the Celtic language. For centuries Bretons have faced a rough and dangerous sea as fishermen. Behind the rocky coast lie the moors, significant in the folklore of the region. For example, one should not walk alone there at night because of the "korrigans," mean trolls who will force you to dance until you fall dead of exhaustion. The Bretons are deeply religious and the region is famed for its religious ceremonies, such as the grand "pardons" or processions, and much psalm singing. People still dance to the *biniou* (or bagpipe), so it is not at all surprising that this lullaby has echoes of Scotch and Welsh music.

TOUTOUIG

Toutouig, la, la, my little child,
   Toutouig, la la.

Your mother is here, little one,
To rock you, little darling.

Your mother is here, little lamb,
To sing you her little song.

The other day you cried a little.
Today you smiled for mother.

Toutouig, la la, poor little one,
It is time to close your tiny eyes.

Toutouig, la la, little rose,
Your cheek next to my heart.

Toutouig, la la, small one,
You must rest your head.

To fly to heaven, little angel,
Do not bat your little wings.

TOUTOUIG

Toutouig, la la, va mabig,
   Toutouig, la la.

Da vamm a zo amañ, koantig,
Ouz da luskellad, mignonig.

Da vamm a zo amañ, oanig.
Dite, o kana he sonig.

En deiz all e ouele, kalzig,
Hag hirio e c'hoara, da vammig.

Toutouig, la la, ta, paourig,
Poent eo serra da lagadig.

Toutouig, la la, bihanig,
Red eo diskuiza da bennig.

Toutouig, la la, rozennig,
Da ziouchod war va halonig.

Da nijal d'an neñv, va êlig,
Na zispleg ket da askellig.

Sleep, Baby, Sleep

IN the 17th century François Couperin, one of the most famous of the French composers, made a rondeau for the clavecin from this traditional melody and called it "Le Dodo, ou L'Amour au Berceau." Nobody knows how far back in French history this little lullaby goes. It has been sung in every part of France by generations of mothers. The traditional image of the chicken, which in this case is used as a note of promise to reward sleep, is widely found in the lullabies of French-speaking peoples throughout the world.

SLEEP, BABY, SLEEP   DODO, L'ENFANT, DO.

Sleep, sleep, baby, sleep.   Dodo, l'enfant, do.
Now then, baby, don't you peep.   L'enfant dormira tantère.
Sleep, sleep, baby, sleep.   Dodo, l'enfant, do.
Baby soon will fall asleep.   L'enfant dormira tantôt.
A white hen rests upon the branch   Une poule blanche est là sur la branche,
Who will lay a little egg   Qui va faire un p'tit coco
For my baby, if he'll sleep.   Pour l'enfant s'il fait do, do.
Baby, baby, go to sleep.   Do, do, l'enfant, do.
Now then go to sleep.   L'enfant dormira tantère.
Sleep, sleep, baby, sleep,   Dodo, l'enfant, do,
It's time you were asleep.   L'enfant dormira tantôt.

Go to Sleep, Colas

"GO to Sleep, Colas" is as widely known as "Do, Do, L'Enfant Do" in the French-speaking world. Here one of the older children tries to lull the younger child to sleep with promises, no doubt expecting at least a share, and should the child actually fall asleep, the lion's share of all the good things to eat and drink.

GO TO SLEEP, COLAS

Go to sleep, Colas, my little brother;
Go to sleep and you will have some milk;
Mama is upstairs making cake,
Papa is downstairs making chocolate.
Go to sleep, Colas, my little brother,
Go to sleep and you will have some milk.

FAIS DODO, COLAS

Fais dodo, Colas, mon p'tit frere;
Fais dodo, t'auras du lolo;
Maman est en haut qui fait du gateau,
Papa est en bas qui fait du chocolat.
Fais dodo, Colas, mon p'tit frere,
Fais dodo, t'auras du lolo.

Hush, Poor Child, Hush
Thee to Sleep

THE BASQUE country is on both sides of the Pyrenees, in France as well as in Spain. The origins of the Basques are veiled in mystery and their language is unique, having no known Indo-European counterparts. Together with their language the Basques have held fast to their customs, traditions and folklore, especially in the mountain sections. Their folk song is most beautiful. The melody of this lullaby and its utter brooding quality are strongly Basque as is the sadness and straight-forward realism of the song's words.

HUSH, POOR CHILD, HUSH THEE TO SLEEP

Hush, poor child, hush thee to sleep;
See him lying in slumber deep!
Thou first, then following I,
We will hush and hush-a-by.
Lo lo lo lo lo lo.

Thy bad father is at the inn;
Oh! the shame of it, and the sin!
Home at midnight he will fare
Drunk with strong wine of Navarre!
Lo lo lo lo lo lo.

AUR GAISHUA LO ETA LO

Aur gaishua lo eta lo,
Lo giro on bat dago!
Zuk orain eta nik gero;
Biyok egingo degu lo.
Lo lo lo lo lo lo.

Aita gaiztoa tabernan dago,
Pikaro! jokalariya!
Laster etorriko da echera
Ardo Naparrez ordiya!
Lo lo lo lo lo lo.

99

In the Hills of Cuscioni

CORSICA is perhaps best known as the birthplace of Napoleon. Its chief language is Italian, but this Mediterranean island has been part of France since 1796, and French is the second language. Superstition remains firmly entrenched among the people of the mountain villages. Divination is widely practiced and even the lullabies partake of augury, often fabulous in its imagination. Prophecy and hopes for the future are often a part of the earliest songs a child hears. If the child is a boy, he may be heralded as a possible avenger in the long-standing tradition of the *vendetta*. However, the tone of "In the Hills of Cuscioni," addressed to a little girl, is more positive, imagining the possibilities of a happy and successful life ahead.

ANDANTE TRANQUILLO

Nelli monti de Cus – cio – ni V'e – ra na – tu una zi – te – dra, ___

E la so ca – ra mam – mo – ni Li fa – chia l'an – nan – na re – dra, ___

E quand' el – la l'annan – na – va Stu ta – len – tu li pre – ga – va. ___

IN THE HILLS OF CUSCIONI

In the hills of Cuscioni
Sat a mother peacefully at the cradle
Watching the tender, sweet face
Of her daughter.
As she rocked she gently sang
Of her baby's future fate.

When you are a big girl
I'll dress you fine;
Then in town you'll show yourself
'Well groomed, with round curls,
In rich stuffs
Made in Corte, lavishly trimmed.

And you will have a husband
Rich in land and herds,
A handsome shepherd boy
Who one day will be mayor
Of all the mountain people
And all the shepherds.

NELLI MONTI DE CUSCIONI

Nelli monti de Cuscioni
V'era natu una zitedra,
E la so cara mammoni
Li fachia l'annannaredra,
E quand' ella l'annannnava
Stu talentu li pregava.

Quandu vo' saretti grandi
Vi faremu lu vestitu,
La camicia, lu bunnedru
E l'imbustu ben guarnitu
Di stu pannu sfinazzatu,
Chi si tesse a Curticchiatu.

Vi daremu lu maritu
Allevatu a li stazzali,
Un bellissimu partitu,
E sarà lu capurali
Di li nostri montagnoli
Pecurai, e capragghioli.

Nightingale with the Black Beak

PORTUGAL, like neighboring Spain, was deeply influenced by its long period of Moorish domination. The Caliphate of Cordova existed from the 8th century until the Moors were finally driven from the Iberian Peninsula during the 13th century. They left behind a distinctive architecture; they introduced the *nora* or waterwheel, which is still widely used for irrigation in rural Portugal. They first brought and cultivated the lemon, orange and fig trees for which Portugal is famous. Small as it is, Portugal has had enormous influence on world history, particularly in exploration and discovery. This lullaby evokes the image of rich darkness. The nightingale is admonished to "leave the berries on the laurel" so that the child can fall asleep.

NIGHTINGALE WITH THE BLACK BEAK

Nightingale with the black beak,
Nightingale with the black beak,
Leave the berries on the laurel tree.
    Oo........, Oo........
Let the child sleep,
Let the child sleep
Because he is just dozing.
    Oo........, Oo........

Sleep, sleep, my child,
Sleep, sleep, my child,
Mother is coming soon.
    Oo........, Oo........
She went to wash
Your swaddling clothes
On the banks of Belém.
    Oo........, Oo........

ROUXINOL DO BICO PRETO

Rouxinol do bico preto,
Rouxinol do bico preto,
Deixa a baga do loureiro.
    Ó...ó, ó...ó.
Deixa dormir o menino,
Deixa dormir o menino.
Que 'stá no sono primeiro.
    Ó...ó, ó...ó.

Dorme, dorme meu menino,
Dorme, dorme meu menino
Que a maezinha logo vem,
    Ó...ó, ó...ó.
Foi lavar os cueirinhos,
Foi lavar os cueirinhos,
A ribeira de Belém.
    Ó...ó, ó...ó.

Sleep, My Little Babe

IN this Malagan lullaby we find a reflection of the Moorish influence that left an indelible mark on the culture of southern Spain. Andalusian music and architecture are dominated by the same oriental spirit. Elaborately decorative as the arches and galleries of the Alhambra are, their essential lines are graceful and unpretentious. In this song, too, the melodic line is fixed, and it is left to the individual singer to decorate the curve of her song with musical ornaments and variations that arise from her own mood and personality.

Duerme, niño ___ chiqui - to; Du-

-er - me, ___ mi al — ma; ___ Duermete, lu - ce - ri - to, De la

ma - — ña - na. ___ Du-erme, niño chi - quito; ___

Duer - me, ___ mi al-ma; Duer - mete, lu - ce - ri - to, ___

De la   ma — — ña — na.

SLEEP, MY LITTLE BABE

Sleep, my little babe;
Sleep, my precious soul;
Sleep all through the night,
My little morning star.

DUERME, NIÑO CHIQUITO

Duerme, niño chiquito;
Duerme, mi alma;
Duérmete, lucerito,
De la mañana.

Hush-a-bye Baby al
Ron, Ron

CASTILE, once a separate kingdom, is a distinctive region within the Spanish culture. The proud Castilians were never really conquered and overrun by the Moors. Thus, unlike much of southern Spain, Castile shows very little Moorish influence. Moreover, the language of Castile has become the model for pronunciation and grammar of "official" Spanish throughout the world. The words of this lullaby telling of the hard life of the miner father and the busy mother are typical of the strain of unflinching and unvarnished realism which characterizes much of Spanish literature and folklore.

HUSH-A-BYE BABY AL RON, RON

Hush-a-bye baby al ron, ron,
Your father is digging coal.
Your mother is making butter.
And cannot give you the breast!

When I was a baby in the cradle,
Words like these lulled me to sleep:
Daddy, Mummy, breast, chi-cha!
And other things like that!

ECHATE, NIÑO AL RON, RON

Echate, niño al ron, ron,
Que tu padre está al carbón
Y tu madre a la manteca
No te puede dar la teta ea.

De pequeñito en la cuna
Me enseñaron á dormir,
Papa, Mama, teta, chi-cha,
Y otras cosi asi ea.

106

Europe

In the Morning the Frost Is So Cold

TWENTE is the easternmost part of the province of Overijssel and has managed to retain many of its traditional ways in spite of extensive industrialization around it. The region has a characteristic dialect which is somewhat different from conventional Dutch, and in the original there is a good deal of subtle and amusing word play in the native dialect. Long ago the region was noted for robbers and highwaymen who roamed the moors. The three horsemen coming out of the woods may allude to these mysterious bandits.

IN THE MORNING THE FROST IS SO COLD

In the morning the frost is so cold,
Frost so cold. Joag-den hop-sa-sa,
Fi-ve-la, fal-de-ral-de-ra.
Rode three horsemen up to my door,
Joag-den hop-sa-sa, fi-ve-la, fal-de-ral-de-ra.
Rode three horsemen up to my door.

Up to my door, on through that wood,
Through that wood. Joag-den hop-sa-sa,
Fi-ve-la, fal-de-ral-de-ra.
Up to my door, on through that wood,
Joag-den, hop-sa-sa, fi-ve-la, fal-de-ral-de-ra.
Up to my door, on through that wood.

MORGENS IS DEN RIEP ZOO KOLD

Morgens is den riep zoo kold
Riep zoo kold. Joag-den hop-sa-sa,
Fi-ve-la, fal-de-ral-de-ra.
Reden dreej ruterkes vuur mien duur,
Joag-den, hop-sa-sa, fi-ve-la, fal-de-ral-de-ra.
Reden dreej ruterkes vuur mien duur.

Vuur mien duur, al duur dat wold,
Duur dat wold. Joag-den hop-sa-sa,
Fi-ve-la, fal-de-ral-de-ra.
Vuur mien duur al duur dat wold,
Joag-den hop-sa-sa, fi-ve-la, fal-de-ral-de-ra.
Vuur mien duur al duur dat wold.

Sleep, Sleep, Little One, Sleep

ALSACE, lying on the border of France and Germany, has been swept over by armies and has changed hands many times. The result is a culture which, while predominantly French, includes Germanic elements even in the language. Curiously, the word for elm, *l'ormeau,* is an old French word not much used today but preserved here by a people who have managed to preserve themselves and their heritage during a long and difficult history. The progression of this song is from the commonplace, lambs in the pen, to the beautiful and fabulous, the events of the golden sky of sleep.

SLEEP, SLEEP, LITTLE ONE, SLEEP

Sleep, sleep, little one, sleep.
The sheep are there outside;
The lambs are in the lambs' pen.
Sleep, little one, so nice and warm.
Sleep, sleep, little one, sleep.

Sleep, sleep, little one, sleep.
Your good angel watches again;
He will gather at the young elm
Beautiful dreams and quiet rest.
Sleep, sleep, little one, sleep.

Sleep, sleep, little one, sleep.
The sheep are in the golden sky.
See the moon and her flock
Which she guides way up high.
Sleep, sleep, little one, sleep.

DORS, DORS, MON PETIT, DORS

Dors, dors, mon petit, dors;
Les moutons sont là dehors,
Les agneaux sont dans l'enclos.
Dors, mon petit, bien au chaud.
Dors, dors, mon petit, dors.

Dors, dors, mon petit, dors;
Ton bon ange veille encore,
Il va cueillir à l'ormeau
Le beau reve et le repos.
Dors, dors, mon petit, dors.

Dors, dors, mon petit, dors;
Les moutons sont au ciel d'or.
Vois la lune et son troupeau
Qu'elle guide tout là haut.
Dors, dors, mon petit, dors.

Hush-a-by, Baby Mine

OF all the languages of Europe, the Czech has had the greatest struggle to survive. Czechs' books have been burned by conquerors. Their freedom of communication has been denied or curtailed. Consequently song became their greatest solace. The Czechs have a national adage which says: "Music was one of the special gifts put into a Czech baby's cradle by the fairies."

Their early songs were not rhymed but depended much on assonance and alliteration for their euphony. In this lullaby *hajej, nynej, dadej,* and *milej* all mean sleep. The language is rich in diminutives, and the rules governing the order of words are extremely flexible. Such freedom makes poetic expression varied and gives the imagination the widest possible play.

HUSH-A-BY, BABY MINE

Hush-a-by, baby mine, peacefully rest.
Mother is rocking thee in thy soft nest.
Hush-a-by, lullaby,
Mother is rocking thee in thy soft nest.

HAJEJ MŮJ ANDÍLKU

Hajej, můj, andílku, hajej a spí,
Matička kolíbá děťátko svy.
Hajej, nynej, dadej, milej!
Matička kolíbá děťátko svy.

111

Hush-a-by, golden one, hush-a-by, sleep.
Close your little eyes.
Hush-a-by, slumber, sleep, my beloved.
Close your precious little eyes.

Hajej, můj zlatoušku, hajej a spí,
Zamhouři maličky očičky svy.
Hajej, dadej, dadej, milej!
Zamhouři maličky očičky svy.

Sleep, Baby, Sleep

NETHERLANDS
Dutch

THE melody of this lullaby is akin to the German "Sleep, Baby, Sleep," with slight differences due to the different syllabic qualities of the text. The same melody and words are also known among Dutch-speaking South Africans. Unlike its German counterpart, the Dutch version concentrates exclusively on the development of the single image of the sheep. Since a large part of their land was wrested from the sea by the building of dikes and canals, the Dutch have a saying: "God created the earth, but the Dutch made Holland."

SLEEP, BABY, SLEEP

Sleep, baby, sleep,
Yonder goes a sheep,
A sheep with small white feet,
It drinks the milk so sweet.
Little sheep with its white wool,
Baby drinks his little belly full.

SLAAP, KINDJE, SLAAP

Slaap, kindje, slaap,
Daar buiten loopt een schaap,
Een schaap met witte voetjes,
Drinkt er de melk zo zoetjes.
Schaapje met zijn witte wol,
Kindje drinkt zijn buikje vol.

Now Then, Sleep My Child

WALLIS, one of Switzerland's 22 cantons, is an area of spectacular natural beauty. Here are found the Matterhorn and, as well, the superb Rhone Valley with its forests and the vineyards whose wines are world renowned. It was in Wallis that Saint Bernard of Menton founded his *Hospice* in the 10th century. The *Hospice* has long been known and celebrated for its rescue work. The famous dogs were first bred and trained here, developing a great skill at pathfinding and at tracking down people lost or buried in snowdrifts and avalanches. Wallis is, like most of Switzerland, multilingual. Roughly two thirds of the people are French-speaking, the remainder using a Swiss-German dialect. "Now Then, Sleep My Child" is in Swiss-German. *Druselibus* is not a name, but an accepted term of playful endearment to children.

NOW THEN, SLEEP MY CHILD

Now then, sleep my child.
In the meadow
The sheep are grazing,
Black and white.
You, my child, they'll want to bite.

Now then, Druselibus!
Come with me
To the hazelnut grove,
Full-laden the bushes will be.
What to do with all I cannot see.

Now then kidlet,
Sweet child, sleep a bit.
How you tremble!
Little one, why?
Only the squire's dog is
  passing by.

NUNNU, CHINDLI, SCHLAF!

Nunnu, Chindli, schlaf!
Uf der Mattun
Weidun d'Schaf,
D'schwarzun und d'wissun chemmid mis
Chind gan bissun.

Nunnu, Druselibus!
Chumm bid miär in d'Haselnuss;
Ich weiss än ganzi Stuidä voll
Und weiss nid,
Wa ich druber soll.

Nunnu, chleinä Gitz!
Härzigs Chindli,
Schlaf än Bitz!
Nunnu reitla!
D's Herrin Hundschin geit da.

113

Sleep, Baby, Sleep

AN authority on German folksong, Franz Magnus Bohme, asserts that this lullaby goes back to the very roots of the German people. The first stanza has never been traced to its origin, but the other verses have been added through the centuries. Just as there are several dialects in every language, so there are variants of native melodies. But all dialects can be traced to the mother tongue. There are many versions of this German lullaby and all are related. Richard Wagner incorporated one of them in his *Siegfried-Idyl* which was written as a birthday gift for his wife. It is scored for small orchestra and first performed in 1870.

SLEEP, BABY, SLEEP

Sleep, baby, sleep,
Thy father tends the sheep.
Thy mother shakes the branches small,
Lovely dreams in showers fall.
Sleep, baby, sleep.

Sleep, baby, sleep,
Across the heavens move the sheep.
The little stars are lambs, I guess,
And the moon is the shepherdess.
Sleep, baby, sleep.

Sleep, baby, sleep.
I'll give to you a sheep.
And it shall have a bell of gold
For you to play with and to hold.
Sleep, baby, sleep.

Sleep, baby, sleep.
Now don't bleat like a sheep,
For then the shepherd's dog will come,
And bite my naughty little one.
Sleep, baby, sleep.

Sleep, baby, sleep,
Go and mind the sheep.
Little black dog go away,
Don't disturb my child, I say.
Sleep, baby, sleep.

SCHLAF, KINDLEIN, SCHLAF

Schlaf, Kindlein, schlaf.
Der Vater hüt't die Schaf.
Die Mutter schüttelt's Bäumelein,
Da fällt herab ein Träumelein.
Schlaf, Kindlein, schlaf!

Schlaf, Kindlein, schlaf.
Am Himmel ziehn die Schaf.
Die Sternlein sind die Lämmerlein,
Der Mond, der ist das Shäferlein.
Schlaf, Kindlein, schlaf!

Schlaf, Kindlein, schlaf.
So schenk' ich dir ein Schaf.
Mit einer goldnen Schelle fein,
Das Soll dein Speilgeselle sein.
Schlaf, Kindlein, schlaf.

Schlaf, Kindlein, schlaf.
Und blöt' nicht, wie ein Schaf.
Sonst kommt des Schäfers Hündelein
Und beiszt mein böses Kindlein.
Schlaf, Kindlein, schlaf.

Schlaf, Kindlein, schlaf.
Geh' fort und hüt die Schaf.
Geh fort, du schwarzes Hündelein
Und weck' mir nicht mein Kindlein.
Schlaf, Kindlein, schlaf!

Schlaf', Kindlein, schlaf'!

Schlaf', Kindlein, schlaf'!
Der Va-ter hüt't die Schaf',
die Mut-ter schüt-telt's Bäu-me-lein,
da fällt her-ab ein Träu-me-lein.
Schlaf', Kindlein, schlaf'!

Schlaf', Kindlein, schlaf'!
Am Himmel zieh'n' die Schaf':
Die Sternlein sind die Lämmerlein,
Der Mond der ist das Schäferlein.
Schlaf', Kindlein, schlaf'!

Schlaf', Kindlein, schlaf'!
So schenk' ich dir ein Schaf
Mit einer goldnen Schelle fein,
Das soll dein Spielgeselle sein.
Schlaf', Kindlein, schlaf'!

Schlaf', Kindlein, schlaf',
Und blöt' nicht, wie ein Schaf:
Sonst kommt des Schäfers Hündelein
Und beißt mein böses Kindlein.
Schlaf', Kindlein, schlaf'!

Schlaf', Kindlein, schlaf'!
Geh' fort und hüt' die Schaf',
Geh' fort du schwarzes Hündelein
Und weck' mir nicht mein Kindelein!
Schlaf', Kindlein, schlaf'!

Ai, Lu Lu

ALTHOUGH the melodies of Polish folk music are often simple, the rhythms are striking and alive, as alive as the rhythms of the native Polish folk dances—the mazurka, the crocovienne, the obertass, and the polonaise. The songs which a Polish mother sings to her child are a fusion of ancient pagan myth and Christian idealism. The cradle here has an almost mythical sig-

nificance for the peasant mother. It is endowed with the power to make or mar a future life, and it is believed to be sinful to rock an empty cradle. If a bird flies over a baby in a cradle, it is conceived of as a certain portent of evil. If the child is then removed from the cradle and put to bed, disaster will follow. Such beliefs have long prevailed in rural districts.

Oj lu lú lu lu lu, Ko-lib-ka zmar-mu-ru, Pie - luszki

zra - becz - ku, lu - laj an - - io - le - czku.

Lu lu, lu lu lu, lu lu, lu lu lu,

Lu lu lu lu _ lu lu lu _ lu lu lu.

AI, LU LU

Ai, lu lu lu lu lu. No cradle of marble,
No pillows of lace for you, my darling.
Lu-lu, lu-lu-lu, lu-lu, lu-lu-lu,
Lu-lu, lu-lu-lu, lu-lu, lu-lu.

Red berries are falling into the water,
And I, my baby, I have no charm.
Lu-lu, lu-lu-lu, lu-lu, lu-lu,
Lu-lu, lu-lu-lu, lu-lu, lu-lu.

Though I'm not beautiful and we'll never be rich,
I ask for nothing, darling, because you are my own.
Lu-lu, lu-lu-lu, lu-lu, lu-lu-lu.
Lu-lu, lu-lu-lu, lu-lu, lu-lu.

OJ, LU LU

Oj lu lu lu lu lu, Kolibka zmarmuru,
Pieluszki zrąbeczku, lulaj anioleczku.
Lu-lu, lu-lu-lu, lu-lu, lu-lu-lu,
Lu-lu, lu-lu-lu, lu-lu, lu-lu.

Czerwone jagody Spadaja do wody,
Jużem przekonany, Że nie mam urody
Lu-lu, lu-lu-lu, lu-lu, lu-lu-lu,
Lu-lu, lu-lu-lu, lu-lu, lu-lu.

Choć urody nie mam, Majątku nie wiele,
I tak was nie proszę, O nic przyjaciele.
Lu-lu, lu-lu-lu, lu-lu, lu-lu-lu,
Lu-lu, lu-lu-lu, lu-lu, lu-lu.

Sleep, Little Soul

THE largest part of Austria is Alpine country. Here a type of song has developed that is of distinct character. The mountain people have made use of a trumpet about six or eight feet in length, known as the Alphorn, which is of utmost importance to them. Its tones reach out to great distances. At dusk its call serves as a warning to men and their herds that night is coming, and the country folk are reminded that the time for singing and evening prayer is at hand. Many Austrian folk songs, of which this lullaby is an example, are not unlike the folk melodies of Germany. The songs were inspired by the school of romantic poetry that flourished in Germany during the late eighteenth and the early nineteenth centuries.

Schlaf, du kleine See – le, schlaf in guter Ruh __

Schlummre oh-ne Feh – le, tu die Augen zu.__ Schlummre sanft und süs – se,

Ruhe Hand' und Füs – se, Auch das Aüge-lein __ muss geschlossen sein. __

SLEEP, LITTLE SOUL

Sleep, little soul, sleep in peace
Sleep without pause, close your eyes.
Sleep soft and sweet,
Rest hands and feet
Eyes must be closed, too.

Sleep little soul, sleep in peace
Sleep without pause, close your eyes.
Like birds in the woods,
Like the shepherd in the moss,
Sleep without fear.

Sleep little soul, sleep in peace
Sleep without pause, close your eyes.
When the angels above
Praise God, the Father
Then I daily glorify God for you.

SCHLAF, DU KLEINE SEELE

Schlaf, du kleine Seele, schlaf in guter
    Ruh
Schlummre ohne Fehle, tu die Augen
    zu.
Schlummre sanft und süsse,
Ruhe Hand' und Füsse,
Auch das Aügelein muss geschlossen
    sein.

Schlaf, du kleine Seele, schlaf in guter
    Ruh
Schlummre ohne Fehle, tu die Augen
    zu.
Schlummre sanft und süsse, wie
    Vöglein im Gebüsche
Wie der Hirt im Moos
Schlummre sorgenlos.

Schlaf, du kleine Seele, schlaf in guter
    Ruh
Schlummre ohne Fehle, tu die Augen
    zu.
Wenn die Englein droben
Gott, den Vater loben
O dann preise ich täglich Gott für dich.

Schlaf, du kleine Seele, schlaf in guter Ruh

Schlaf, du kleine Seele, schlaf in guter Ruh,
schlummre ohne Fehle, tu die Augen zu!
Schlummre sanft und süße,
ruhe Händ' und Füße,
auch das Augelein
muß geschlossen sein!

Schlaf, du kleine Seele, schlaf in guter Ruh,
schlummre ohne Fehle, tu die Augen zu!
Schlummre sanft und süße, wie
Vöglein im Gebüsche,
wie der Hirt im Moos,
schlummre sorgenlos!

Schlaf, du kleine Seele, schlaf in guter Ruh,
schlummre ohne Fehle, tu die Augen zu!
Wenn die Englein droben
Gott, den Vater, loben,
o dann preise ich
täglich Gott für dich.

The Sun Is Setting

ALTHOUGH the Hungarians have a rich and varied treasury of folk music, lullabies, as such, do not exist in that literature. The peasants are an agricultural people working a stubborn soil and they find little spare time to devote to infants. Babies are usually taken out into the fields, sometimes in a convenient wheelbarrow, and left to their own devices until nurs-ing time. In the evening, when the mother has some time for the child, she is apt to sing a folk song. Often, only the melody is retained and new words are sub-stituted—words that are a spontaneous outpouring of the mother's feelings. In this song we see her attempt to awaken the child's interest in the simple beauties of nature—the sky, fields, flowers and the bird song.

ANDANTINO GIOCOSO

Alkonyodik már a nap, Minden nagyobb árnyat kap, Fakón a kis madár sereg,

Takarodót csi-cse-reg. Fakón a kis madár sereg, Ta-ka-ro-dót csi-cse-reg.

AD LIBITUM

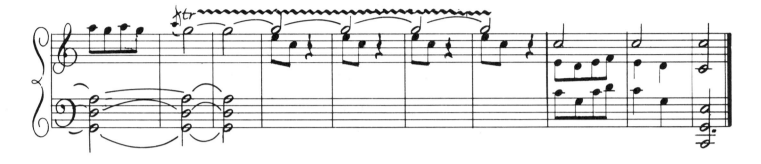

THE SUN IS SETTING   ALKONYODIK MAR Á NAP

The sun is setting,   Alkonyodik már a nap,
Shadows are lengthening,   Minden nagyobb árnyat kap,
And on the trees swarms of birds   Fakón a kis madár sereg,
Sing their evening song.   Takarodót csicsereg.

The flowers are so sleepy   A virág oly álmos már,
That their heads sway right and left. Feje jobbra–balra jár,
We, too, can stroll home   Én is ballaghatok hát,
And say: Good night, sweet Nature.   Szép természet jójszakát.

Hush-a-bye, My Lovely Child

THIS lovely slumber song comes from a city with a renowned cultural history and tradition. Its university, founded in the 11th century, is the oldest in all of Italy. Here such literary luminaries as Dante, Petrarch, and Tasso were students. The learned musical scholar, Padre Martini, lived in Bologna and, as a result, the city became a place of pilgrimage for musicians from countries far and near. Young Mozart, who was not quite fourteen when he came to Bologna, was urged by Padre Martini to take a test in composition at the Philharmonic Academy. At this solemn occasion Mozart was given a theme to elaborate upon, and he came through with flying colors. This test piece (K 86) is now in the Bologna Philharmonic Academy.

Bologna

HUSH-A-BYE, MY LOVELY CHILD

Hush-a-bye, my lovely child,
Hush-a-bye my lovely child,
Hush, hush, my little one.

Sleep sweetly my lovely child,
Sleep sweetly my lovely child,
Hush, hush my little one.

FI LA NANA, E MI BEL FIOL

Fi la nana, e mi bel fiol,
Fi la nana, e mi bel fiol,
Fa si la nana.

Dormi ben, e mi bel fiol,
Dormi ben, e mi bel fiol,
Fa si la nana.

Sleep Until Dawn

SICILY, the largest island of the Mediterranean, easily exposed to invasion in the past, has been deeply influenced by many cultures which have left their mark on the land, the language, and indeed, upon the faces of the people. Greek, Saracen and Roman domination in ancient times have also left their im-

print. This lullaby is well known among the peasants. The original words are in the Sicilian dialect which is quite different from continental Italian. There is a rather wide possibility for ornamentation of the basic melody, depending largely on the mother's mood. That she wishes sleep would come quickly is certain.

MODERATO DOLCEMENTE

SLEEP UNTIL DAWN

Sleep until dawn!
How beautiful your name is!
He who gave it to you is a fine fellow.
Bo, bo, bo, bo.
Sleep, little one, go to sleep.

Sleep until dawn!
Let sleep come.
Come on horseback, come not on foot.
Bo, bo, bo, bo.
Sleep, little one, go to sleep.

ER A LA VÒ

Er a la vò.
Che beddu stu nomu.
Cu ci lu misi e un glantumu.
Bo, bo, bo, bo,
Durmi nicu e fa la vò.

Er a la vò.
Sunnuzzu veni,
Veni a cavaddu e veniri a peri.
Bo, bo, bo, bo,
Durmi nicu e fa la vò.

Southeast Europe

You Are as Ruddy as an Orange!

TOGETHER with the Serbians and the Slovenians, the Croats form one of the major cultural groups in the composite nation of Yugoslavia. Basically agricultural and peace-loving, the Croatians never had, prior to modern times, the kind of military tradition which their neighbors developed over centuries of defending themselves. The Croatians are noted for their colorful native costumes and are special among the other neighboring Slavic peoples in their use of the Latin rather than the Cyrillic alphabet. All aspects of this lullaby—the stormy sea winds, the beech tree with its cradle—are homely and familiar, except for the orange, which is rare in this region. Thus, by implication, it is the child who is rare, lovely and wonderful, a perfect gift.

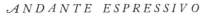

YOU ARE AS RUDDY AS AN ORANGE!

You are as ruddy as an orange!
Were you born on an orange tree?
No, I was not born on an orange tree,
But my dearest mother bore me.
I was cradled in the beech tree,
Stormy winds rocked me
From Uchka to the sea.

*Hush–a–by

RUMENA SI KAKO I NARANČA

Rumena si kako i naranča;
Ili ti je naranča rodila?
"Nije mene naranča rodila,
Već je mene mila majka moja.
Bukva mi je za zikvicu bila,
Zibala me od Učke do mora."

*Nanaj

129

Sleep, Little Anna

DALMATIA is situated on the rugged and beautiful western coastline of Yugoslavia, hemmed in on one side by the mountains and facing the blue sparkle of the Adriatic Sea. The Dalmatians are an ancient people, a fact attested to by a biblical reference (II Timothy 4:10) telling of a trip made there by Titus. The Venetian occupation (1718–1814) left its imprint in the delicate arcades and fine squares. These days Dalmatia is part of the region of Croatia and the spoken language is a west Croatian dialect. Two characteristics of this lyric are of special note in this collection. First, though folklore, it is at once sophisticated and as complex as poetry. Moreover, it is very rare among lullabies to give a tender account in poetic terms of the mother's love for the father. In a sense it doubles as a love song. Perhaps one may assume the father is a listener to the lullaby.

ANDANTINO

Spa- vaj mi, spavaj Anci- ce Spa- vaj mi, spavaj Anci- ce Spa-

vaj mi, spavaj Anci- ce Na kri - lu svoje majci- ce!

Tu - li- pan, jor- go- van, To su cvi - ta dva,

Vo - li - lo - se   dvo - je mla - dih   K'o dva go - lu - ba. _____

SLEEP, LITTLE ANNA

Sleep, little Anna, sleep,
Sleep, little Anna, sleep,
Sleep, little Anna, sleep,
On your mother's lap!

    The tulip, the lilac,
    These are two flowers;
    A young couple loved each other
    Like two doves.

Your mother will sleep,
Your mother will sleep,
Your mother will sleep.
I will kiss you, darling.

    The tulip, the lilac,
    These are two flowers;
    You, dear one,
    Shall I never forget.

Those two dark eyes of yours
Which gazed at me,
Those honey lips of yours
Which kissed me.

    The tulip, the lilac,
    These are two flowers;
    You, dear one,
    Shall I never forget.

SPAVAJ MI, ANČICE

Spavaj mi, spavaj Ančice,
Spavaj mi, spavaj Ančice,
Spavaj mi, spavaj Ančice
Na krilu svoje majčice!

    Tulipan, jorgovan,
    To su cvita dva,
    Volilo se dvoje mladih
    K'o dva goluba.

Tvoja će majka spavati,
Tvoja će majka spavati,
Tvoja će majka spavati,
Ja ću te, dušo, ljubiti.

    Tulipan, jorgovan,
    To su cvita dva,
    Tebe, draga,
    Zaboravit neću nikada.

Ta tvoja crna oka dva,
Koja su mene gledala,
Ta tvoja medna ustasca,
Koja su mene ljubila.

    Tulipan, jorgovan,
    To su cvita dva,
    Tebe, draga,
    Zaboravit neću nikada.

O John, My Son!

IT is most significant that this Serbian lullaby alludes to the child as "my Easter lamb," for among the devout Serbian people Easter is the greatest festival of the year. After a rigorous Lenten season, characterized by rituals of purification and solemn reflection, on Easter Sunday the villagers arise very early in the morning and set off in the dark for church. Entering the church, each parishioner kisses the icon, then places an offering of spring flowers nearby. The climax of the ceremony is a procession led by the priest with all the congregation carrying brightly lit candles. Thus in this slumber song, the child is given a vision of the great festival to dream on. The Serbians are Greek Orthodox and their language is Slavonic. But this lullaby, "Oh John, My Son," is from Old Serbia, a region south and southeast of Belgrade. Its language is the South Serbian dialect.

Ti - si - mi   sin - ko _____   pr - ve - — nats,

O JOHN, MY SON!

O John, my son John,
O John, my Johnnie!
O John, my son John,
O John, my Johnnie!
Thou art my dearest, my firstborn son,
Thou are my dearest, my firstborn son.

O John, my son John,
O John, my Johnnie!
O John, my son John,
O John, my Johnnie!
Thou art my lambkin, my Easter lamb,
Thou are my lambkin, my Easter lamb.

O John, my son John,
O John, my Johnnie!
O John, my son John,
O John, my Johnnie!
Thou art my posy of sweet spring flow'rs,
Thou art my posy of sweet spring flow'rs.

YOVANE, SINE

Yovane, sine,
Yovane, mori,
Yovane, sine,
Yovane, lele.
Ti si mi sinko prvenats,
Ti si mi sinko prvenats.

Yovane, sine,
Yovane, mori,
Yovane, sine,
Yovane, lele.
Ti si mi yagnye djurdjevsko,
Ti si mi yagnye djurdjevsko.

Yovane, sine,
Yovane, mori,
Yovane, sine,
Yovane, lele.
Ti si mi tsveche prolochno,
Ti si mi tsveche prolochno.

Јоване, сине

Јоване, сине,
Јоване, мори,
Јоване, сине,
Јоване, леле.

Ти си ми синко првенац,
Ти си ми синко првенац,

Јоване, сине,
Јоване, мори,
Јоване, сине,
Јоване, леле.

Ти си ми јагње ђурђевско,
Ти си ми јагње ђурђевско,

Јоване, сине,
Јоване, мори,
Јоване, сине,
Јоване, леле.

Ти си ми цвеће пролећно.
Ти си ми цвеће пролећно.

Nani, Nani, Mother's Little Baby

THE Bulgarian people live in the northeastern part of the rugged Balkan Peninsula. The soil is rich and fruitful and has prompted a largely agricultural economy. The Bulgarian peasant, not yet much affected or distracted by urbanization, has been able to keep his heritage of folklore intact. Music is a significant part of the folk customs and ceremonies, and thus there are many categories of Bulgarian folk music—heroic songs, ballads, and epics. There are many songs which deal with the ordinary, day-to-day life of the peasants, songs of ploughing and harvest, wedding songs, and many songs designed especially to be sung by and to children.

NANI, NANI, MOTHER'S LITTLE BABY

Nani, nani, Mother's little baby,
Slumber, come from the forest grove,
Take my Tzochko by his small hand.

Lead him with you to the grove,
Cradle him in the soft grasses,
Cradle him in the soft grasses.

Cover him with warmest fern leaves,
While I rock him, tenderly singing, swinging, singing,
Nani, nani, Mother's little baby.

NÁNI MI, NÁNI, MÁMINO DETÉ

Náni mi, náni, mámino deté,
Elá súnio ot gorítsa,
Fáni Tsóchka za ruchítsa.

Zavedí go vav gorítsa,
Postelí mu trevítsa,
Postelí mu trevítsa.

Zavíí go sas pápritsa
Kató go lĩuleĩa i mu sládko péĩa:
Náni mi, náni, mámino deténtse.

Нáни ми, нáни, мáмино дéте,
Елá сънйо от горѝца,
фáни Цóчка за ръчѝца.

Заведѝ го във горѝца,
Постéли му тревѝца,
Постéли му тревѝца.

Завѝй го със пáприца
Катó го люлéя и му слáдко пéя:
Нáни ми, нáни, мáмино детéнце.

Lully, Lully, Lully

MONTENEGRO acquires its name from the large black mountain (*Montanagro* in Italian, *Crna Gora* in Serbo-Croatian) which shields its people and the small mountainous area which they inhabit. Of all the Slavic people on the Balkan Peninsula, the Montenegrans were the most successful in resisting Turkish conquest and domination because of their extremely mountainous terrain and their ability as guerrilla fighters. They are closely related to the Serbs by their Greek Orthodoxy with all its ritual and by their culture and their language.

LULLY, LULLY, LULLY	LYULYALA, LYULYALA	Љуљала, љуљала мајка синана
Lully, lully, lully Mummy her little son Is rocking. Mummy her little son Is rocking. Sleep is eluding baby!	Lyulyala, lyulyala mayka sinana, Lyulyala, lyulyala mayka sinana, Ninana, sinana San te prevario, Ninana, sinana San te prevario.	Љуљала, љуљала мајка синана, Љуљала, љуљала мајка синана, Нинана, синана Сан те преварио, Нинана, синана Сан те преварио.
Are you sleeping? Here comes father. Are you sleeping? Here comes father, And towards thee Comes a drowsy grandmother.	Priye tebe Nego baba tvoga, Priye tebe Nego baba tvoga, Otud ide Sanovita baka.	Прије тебе Него баба твога, Прије тебе Него баба твога, Отуд иде Сановита бака.

Thy grandmother pushes	Ona vozi	Она вози
A sleigh carriage	Tvoya kola sanka.	Твоја кола санка.
Full of dreams.	Poshto, bako,	Пошто, бако,
What price, grandmother?	Tvoya kola sanka?	Твоја кола санка?
Four golden coins	Ova sanka	Ова санка
For all dreams.	Chetiri dukata.	Четири дуката.
Jovan's mother	Kupuye nyikh	Купује њих
The dreams did buy,	Yovanova mayka,	Јованова мајка,
And now asleep	Pa nyikh tura	Па њих тура
In the sleigh-carriage	Yovu u beshiku;	Јову у бешику;
Is her Jovo,	Zaspa Yovo	Заспа Јово
Like a little lamb.	Kao yagnye malo.	Као јагње мало.

Come, Hush-a-by, Hush, Hush

PROBABLY no other country in Europe is more a meeting place of east and west than Rumania. It was long believed that the Rumanian people were descendants of Roman colonists in Dacia. This theory has come into question in recent years, but there is no doubt that the Rumanian language is an ancient Romance tongue, now strongly colored by Slavonic and

Turkish influence. Language is not Rumania's only tie with Western Europe. The people bear little resemblance to their Slavic neighbors in appearance or way of life. Bucharest strives successfully to be another Paris despite eastern elements in architecture, folklore, and music. Rumania's culture still shows evidence to this day of its origins and roots in the Romance world.

Moldavia

Ca ma — — ma te o le — — ga - na.

Ca — — ma te — o le ga — — na.

COME, HUSH-A-BY, HUSH, HUSH

Come, hush-a-by, hush, hush.
Come, hush, with mommy,
Since mommy is rocking you.
Since mommy is rocking you.

And from the throat she sings to you.
Hush, hush, with mommy.
Come, hush, hush-a-by,
Since mommy is holding you close.

With bread and with olives,
Come, hush-to-sleep with mommy.
Come, hush, mommy's little darling,
Come, hush, mommy's little darling.

AIDI, NANI, NANI, NANI

Aidi, nani, nani, nani.
Aidi, nani, cu mama,
Că mama te-o legāna.
Că mama te-o legāna.

Si din gură ţ-o cînta
Nani, nani, cu māma,
Haidi nani, nanita
Cá mama te-o ţine bine.

Cu pine şi cu māsline.
Aidi nani, cu māmita,
Aidi nani, puiu mamii.
Aidi nani, puiu mamii.

Now, Then, Sleep, Sleep, My Child

THE cradle song with its cry of "Nani, Nani, Nani" is found throughout Greece in a wide variety of versions. Many ancient superstitions persist in Greek folklore and observances. For example, in Athens' countryside there is still prevalent the old notion that on the third night following the birth of a child he is visited by the *Moirai*, the three fates who will decide the future fortunes and misfortunes of the child and the length of his life. Although the period and time of visitation varies according to the district of the country, the manner of receiving these supernatural visitors seems to be universal. Dogs must be kept tied up. All superfluous furniture must be removed, lest they should trip. They are propitiated by a banquet of cakes, honey, bread, and wine. Sometimes even gold and silver are left, as though even the fates are susceptible to a bribe. The convention of the promise of kingdoms to the child is an old one. It was referred to by the Latin poet Horace in the first of his *Epistles* as "the lullaby of children which promises a kingdom to those who are good." Ironically, the ancient Greeks did indeed once own the fabled cities of Cairo, Constantinople, and Alexandria.

NOW, THEN, SLEEP, SLEEP, MY CHILD

Now, then, sleep, sleep, my child,
Sleep and dream, my lovely child.
I'll give you the city of Alexandria
  in sugar,
All of Cairo in rice,
And rich Constantinople,
And there you shall reign for three
  years.

AÍDE, AÍDE KIMÍSOU, KÓRI MOU

Aíde, aíde kimísou, kóri mou,
K'eghó k'eghó ná soú kharíso tín
Alexańdra zákhari
Ké tó ké tó Misíri rízi
Ké tín Konstanti noúpoli
Trís khrónous ná tín rízis.

ΑΙΝΤΕ, ΑΙΝΤΕ ΚΟΙΜΗΣΟΥ, ΚΟΡΗ ΜΟΥ

Αἴντε, αἴντε κοιμήσου, κόρη μου
κι ἐγώ, κι ἐγώ νά σοῦ χαρίσω
τήν Ἀλεξάνδρα ζάχαρη
καί τό, καί τό Μισῆρι ρύζι
καί τήν Κωνσταντινούπολη
τρεῖς χρόνους νά τήν ρίζης.

O, Saint Marina,
Patroness

THE island of Cyprus is rich in myth and history. It was here, according to legend, that Aphrodite, Goddess of Love, emerged in all her beauty from the foam of the sea, and her worship began at Paphos on the slopes of the hills beyond. The actual history of the island dates back to the sixth millennium B.C. Today the Madonna and Child, a fusion of the early worship of Aphrodite with Christianity and a surrender of the pagan to the

newer faith, is a typical image for the island culture. Saint Marina, addressed in the opening stanza, is the patron saint of expectant mothers. She is also the special protector of all children. She exemplifies the ideal and all that is beautiful in mother and child. She is seen all over Cyprus today, represented in Byzantine iconography. The second stanza projects the hope that the son will keep his eyes and his mind open to all learning.

A - ya Marina je ji - ra - pou Poji - mizis ta mo - ra Ro-

mavis' ta kso - por - kia mou ___ Na - ji - mi - thi o yokas mou.

Khate na ka - mi a _____

O, SAINT MARINA, PATRONESS

O, Saint Marina, patroness,
Who sends all little ones to sleep,
Please bolt and lock our gates and
    doors
And lull to sleep my little boy.
Now let him murmur a—a—a.

Let him sleep and then wake again,
And then get up', and start to walk,
And then to take his pen and paper
And go to a good teacher soon,
To learn his Alpha, Beta too,
And to grow wise and diligent.

AYÁ MARÍNA JE JÍRA

Ayá Marína je jíra
Póu pojimízis tá mórá
Románis' ta ksopórkia mou
Ná jimithí o yókas mou.
Kháte ná kámi á—á—á.

Ná jimithí, n' anayothí,
Ná sikothí, na parpatí,
Ná pkiási pénnan jé kharatín
Ná pá stón tháskalon eftís,
Ná máthi t'Álfa jé tó ví,
Ná váli noún jé prokopín.

ΆΓΙΑ ΜΑΡΙΝΑ ΤΖΙΑΙΤΖΙΡΑ

Ἁγιά Μαρίνα τζιαίτζιρα
ποὺ ποτζιοιμίζεις τὰ μωρά
ρομάνισ᾽τά ξωπόρκια μου
νά τζιοιμηθῇ ὁ γιόκας μου.
Χάτε νά κάμῃ ἄ, ἄ, ἄ.

Νά τζιοιμηθῇ, ν᾽ἀναγιωθῇ,
νά σηκωθῇ, νά παρπατῇ,
νά πκιάσῃ πένναν τζιαί χαρτίν,
νά πᾶ στόν δασκαλον εὐφτής.
Νά μάθῃ τ᾽ Ἀλφα τζιαί τό Βί,
νά βάλῃ νοῦν τζιαί προκοπήν.

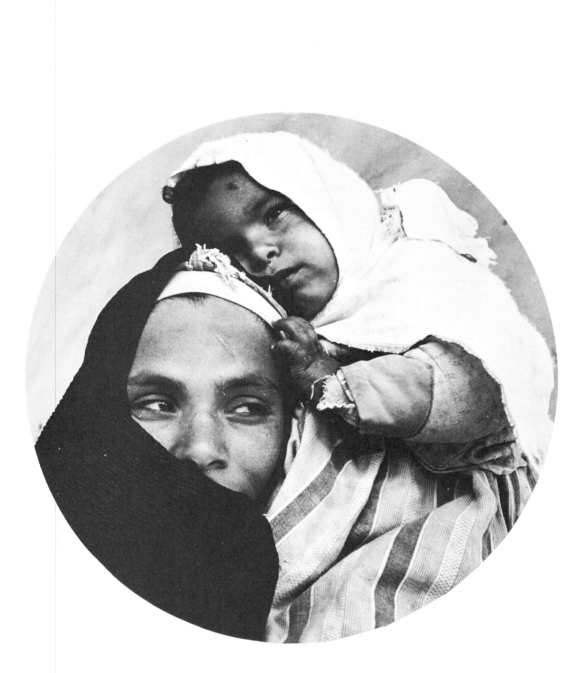

North Africa

Sleep, Sleep

AN ancient country which has known many conquerors, Tunisia is now a free state. Even before Roman conquest, the Carthaginians, realizing the land's naval and strategic importance, occupied Tunisia. After the Roman occupation the Moslem rulers exploited this advantage. Even as late as the 16th century, Moors, exiled from Spain, and Turkish *corsairs* established a pirate bastion on Tunisia's Barbary Coast, preying on Mediterranean merchant ships for several centuries. Finally, in 1956, Tunisia achieved independence from France. The majority of Tunisians are Sunnites, the orthodox or traditionalist branch of the Moslem faith. The reference to poppies in this lullaby is a natural one, for poppies are extensively grown southeast of Tunis.

SLEEP, SLEEP

Sleep, sleep
Sleep is winning over you
O little cheeks like poppies
Sleep, sleep, slumber
O little flowers of my eyes

NÍNNÍ NÍNNÍ

Nīnnī, nīnnī
Jā kan noum
Yā khouday-yad bougar'oūn
Nīnnī, nīnnī, nīnnī
Yā yā nawwa rat'ay nay-ya-h

ندّى ندّى ندّى

ندّى ندّى ندّى

جاك النوم

يا خديد يا بوقدون

ندّى ندّى ندّى

يا نوارة عينيه

O Rari, O Rari

MOROCCO, a land of sultry days and cool nights, has attracted tourists for decades with its varied climate. The Atlas Mountains provide summer skiing slopes and the Mediterranean coastline provides winter swimming areas. Although Morocco is relatively young as a nation, its history and traditions go back to Biblical days. The earliest inhabitants were the Berbers, whose architecture and handicrafts are still extant in villages throughout the country. Rabat, the capital city of

Morocco, stands as a fine modern city in striking contrast to the contiguous old Moorish city with its royal palace and luxuriant gardens. The Moroccan child, like infants the world over, is often restive and wakeful. To aid sleep, the mother rocks her child gently and lifts her voice in a melancholic monotone. The words "O rari" signify the bringer of sleep. Sometimes the mother begs the intervention of Allah, the Supreme Being, and implores his protection and guidance over her child.

146

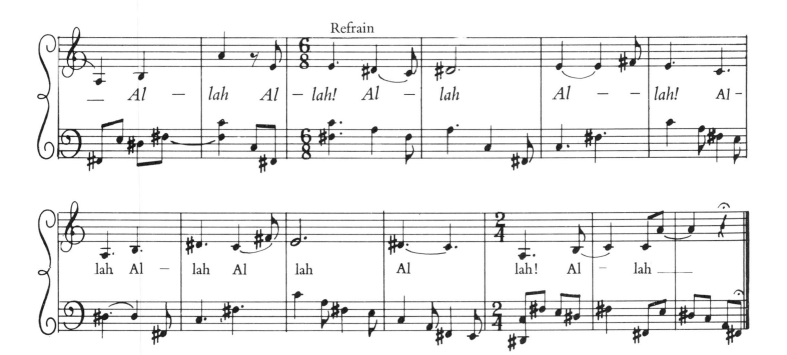

O RARI, O RARI

O Rari, O Rari
O you! who puts children to sleep,
Put my little one to sleep
On the high bed.
Allah Allah! Allah Allah!

I need him to sleep.
I beg my God to guide him
And lead him and protect him
And keep Satan away from him
Allah Allah! Allah Allah!

YĀ-RĀ-RĪ

Yā-Rā-rī Ya bar-bari
Ya nah has al dra-ri
Na-has li wa ledi
Fouk el firash el ali
Allah Allah! Allah Allah!

Rana felhaji fih
Nelleb rabbi yehdih
Ydhdih wa yardih
Wa yebik el shaytan alayhi
Allah Allah! Allah Allah!

يــارري يا بربــرى٠٠٠٠ى٠٠٠٠ى٠٠٠٠ى

يــارري يا بربــرى٠٠٠٠ى٠٠٠٠ى٠٠٠٠ى
يــا نعلــس الدرارى٠٠٠٠ى٠٠٠٠ى٠٠٠٠ى
نــعــاس لــى ولــدى٠٠٠٠ى٠٠٠٠ى٠٠٠٠ى
فــوق لفرش العــا لــى٠٠ى٠٠ى٠٠١٠٠١الله

ر نــافلحجى فى٠٠٠٠يــ٠٠٠٠٠٠يــ٠٠٠٠٠ه
نظلب ربى يهدى٠٠٠٠يــ٠٠٠٠يــ٠٠٠٠يه
يهديــه و يرضيــــ٠٠٠٠يــ٠٠٠٠يه
و يبعد الشيطان عيــــ٠٠يـ٠٠يه٠٠٠١٠٠١الله

Harara Yourara!

THE Mzouda Tribe occupies the mountain fastness of the Atlas range in the northeastern section of Algeria. Whereas many of the Berbers were assimilated in the Arab conquests of the 7th century, this tribe and several others of Berber stock were able to preserve much of their traditional cultural and language patterns by fleeing to relatively protected pockets in the Grand Atlas range. The Mzoudas are principally an agricultural people who divide labor by sex, with the men doing the hunting, fishing, and herding while the women pick wild fruits and vegetables, gather shellfish, and milk the livestock. All in all, the Mzoudas are also remarkably egalitarian, and serfdom and slavery are practically unknown to these mountain dwellers. In keeping with this fact is the notably democratic nature of the tribal government, all authority being vested in an assembly (*jemen*) composed of all adult males. And, as this lullaby reveals, Mzouda parents are capable of a tenderly humorous attitude toward their offspring. Clearly the mother is at her wit's end in offering this "gruel" to her child. The Mzouda mother wraps her infant in a shawl which she fastens to her back. The melody of this lullaby is repetitive in its pattern, relieved by ornamentation which is entirely a spontaneous improvisation. All the while she sways back and forth, back and forth.

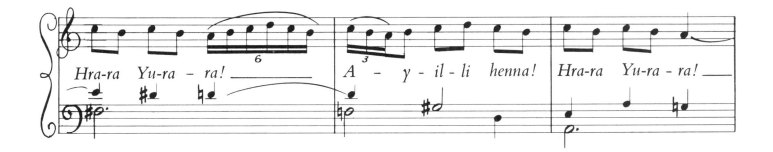

Berber
Mzouda Tribe

A - yi -wi hen - na! Hra-ra Yu-ra-ra!

HARARA YOURARA!

Harara yourara!
Oh my darling daughter!
Harara yourara!
Oh my darling son!
I will mix your gruel,
And grind some flies into it,
And give it to you so that you'll be
 satisfied!
Harara yourara!
Oh my darling daughter!
Harara yourara!
Oh my darling son!

HRA-RA YU-RA-RA!

Hra-ra yu-ra-ra!
A-y-illi henna!
Hra-ra yu-ra-ra!
A-yiwi henna!
Ad rwiǵ taǧw ella,
Nbelg ak gi s izan,
Fkeǵ ak at tšebeet!
Hra-ra yu-ra-ra!
A-y-illi henna!
Hra-ra yu-ra-ra!
A-yiwi henna!

حدارا يوارا

حدارا يوارا
ايلّى حنـا
حوارا يوارا
ايوى حنا
ادرويج تجولاّ
نبلفك جسيندان
فكفك اتسبيت
ايوى حنا
ادرويج تجولاّ
نبلفك جسيندان
فكفك اتسبيت

Sleep, Oh My Beloved Son

ONCE a Spanish colonial possession, Ifni is a small and narrow strip of land, roughly 150 square miles, on the west coast of Africa, just south of Morocco. Its name comes from one Sidi Ifni (meaning "Honorable Sir" Ifni). The Spanish word *señor* is adopted from Sidi. The land itself is harsh and barren, and the major-

ity of the population cluster along the coastline, depending on fishing and the cultivation of barley for subsistence. Nomadic Arab and Berber herdsmen drive their camels and sheep across the inland area, searching for good grazing land or possible trading. The words and script of this lullaby come to us from the Arabic.

SLEEP, OH MY BELOVED SON	NOH NO A IUI HENA	نو نو ا یوی حنا
Sleep, oh my beloved son,	Noh no a iui hena	بو بو ا یوی حنا
Sleep! How beautiful thou art.	Noh no iqad etfulqit	نو نو اقد ا تفلقت
Sleep! Here comes your father.	Noh no ysqad baq	بو بو بشقد حق
Sleep! How beautiful thou art!	Noh no iqad etfulqit	نو نو اقد ا تفلقت

O Creator

THIS song, which combines religious sentiment with a mother's affection, comes from a country with a long and interesting history. The Romans visited what is now the eastern province of Constantine, and remnants of their amphitheaters, temples, and arches still draw prime attention from visitors to the country. Algiers, the capital of Algeria, is famous for its narrow, picturesque streets which lead up to the Casbah (fort) and were built in the sixteenth century. Most of the country's dense population is situated in the Tell or Mediterranean coastal region with its lovely subtropical climate, rich vegetation, Berber forts, and the romantic city of Djidjelli, formerly the stronghold of the pirate Barbarossa. The population is mainly Mohammedan. The tribal life in Algeria is still strong, although many of the traditional ways are changing.

O CREATOR	YĀ BĀRI	يـا بـاري يـا بـاري
O Creator, O Creator,	Yā bāri yā bāri	يـا رقّـاد الـذراري
Thou who puts children to sleep,	Ya reg-ḡad d-dra-ri	تـرقّـد لـي ولـيـدي
Make my little one sleep	Treg-ged li u-li di	بـين الـورد الـغـالـي
Amid precious roses.	Bayn el ward el ga-li	تـرقّـد لـي ولـيـدي
Make my little one sleep	Tregged li u-li-di bayn	بـين الـورد الـغـالـي
Amid precious roses.	El ward el ḡa-li	

I Pray to Allah

EGYPT has a civilization stretching back six or seven thousand years. The geography of the Nile Valley offered particularly favorable conditions for the early establishment of agriculture and the rise of a large population in a small area, surrounded by great deserts. Today Egypt is often viewed as the cultural center of the Arab world. Mohammedanism is the dominant faith, a legacy of the Arab conquest. It should be remembered that ancient Egypt had a highly developed music with instruments ranging from drums to harps, flutes and trumpets. Egyptian music formed the source of Greek music which, in turn, led to the development of occidental music, as cultivated in Alexandria, a center of early Christian worship.

Oooo __ Enshallàh tenaàm enshallàh te-naàm Wadbàh lak go zeén ha-mam

Matkhàf-shi yà-di: el ha-mam Badehàk aà-leh aà-lashian ye-naàm

Oooo Enshallàh téscot en shallàh tés-còt Wadebàh lak go zeén còt-còt

Matkhàf-shi yà di el cot-cot Badehàk aà-leh aà-lashian yen-àes

152

I PRAY TO ALLAH

Oooo . . . . .
I pray to Allah, I pray to Allah
I shall capture for you a pair of pigeons
Don't fear little pigeons. I've said this only
To urge my little one to sleep
I pray to Allah, I pray to Allah
I shall capture for you, two chickens
Don't fear dear chickens. I've said this only
To urge my little one to sleep
I pray to Allah, I pray to Allah
I shall capture for you, two little chicks
Don't fear little chicks. I've said this only
So that my little one will now sleep
Oooo . . . . .

ENSHALLÀH TENAÀM

Oooo
Enshallàh tenaàm enshallàh tenaàm
Wadbàh lak gozeén hamam
Matkhàfshi yàdi el hamam
Badehàk aàleh aàlashian yenaàm
Enshallàh tenàes enshallàh tenàes
Wadbàh lak gozeén khònfess
Badehàk aàleh aàlashian yenàes
Enshallàh téscot enshallàh téscot
Wadebàh lak gozzéen còtcòt
Matkhàfshi yadi el còtcòt
Badehàk aàleh aàleh aàlashian yescot
Oooo

انشــــالله تنـــام

ـــوه ..
انشــالله تنام   ..   انشالله تنـــام
ودبح لك جـــوزيـــن حمـــــــام
ما تخافش يادى الحمـــــام
بد حك عليـــه علشان ينـــــام

انشا لله تنعس   ..   انشا لله تنعس
ودبح لك جـــوزين خنفـــــس
ما تخافشى يادى الخنفـــــس
بد حك عليـــه علشان ينعـــلى

انشا لله تسكت   ..   انشا لله تسكت
ودبح لك جـــوزين كتكــــت
بد حك عليه علشان يسكـــت
هــــوه ..

153

Ushururu My Child Ushururu

STANDING as the gateway between Africa and the Middle East, Ethiopia is the oldest independent nation in Africa. The Emperor, Haile Selassie I, is the 225th ruler in an unbroken chain going back to Menelik, son of King Solomon and the Queen of Sheba. Most of the people in the central highlands are members of the Coptic Church, not unlike the Eastern Orthodox Church, whose liturgical music, *ziema,* is within the ancient oral tradition of Hebraic liturgical song and is passed on from one generation to the next. There is a strong tradition of folk music as well. Many instru-

ments are used to accompany song and dance. Among them are the *begena* or harp, having eight or ten strings and played with two pieces of polished horn; the *kirar* or lyre, of six or ten strings; the *masenko* or viol, with only one string and played with a bow. Drums also are used, and particularly noteworthy are the deep-toned drums used by the Coptic priests in the celebration and ceremony of *Maskal* on September 27th. This lullaby is known throughout Ethiopia. The language is Amharic, one of the Hamito-Semitic languages. The script stems from the early script of South Arabia.

USHURURU MY CHILD USHURURU

Ushururu my child ushururu
Ushururu little baby ushururu

You are on my back when I grind
You are on my back when I spin
My back is sore, get down my little baby

Baby's mother will come back soon
On the donkey's back with bread and milk in her arms

My little baby stay with your father
Ushururu my child ushururu
Ushururu little baby ushururu

USHURURU MAMMO USHURURU

Ushururu mammo ushururu
Ushururu lidge Ushururu

Sifechim aziye, sifetlim aziye
Jerbaye telate nawured mamuye

Yemamuye enat, tolo neyilet
Wetetun beguya dabowun bahiya yizechilet

Lije dehna eder, kabatih eder
Ushururu mammo ushururu
Ushururu lidje ushururu

ኡሹሩሩ ማሞ ሉሹሩሩ

ኡሹሩሩ ልጇ ኡሹሩ
ኡሹሩሩ ማሞ ኡሹሩሩ

ስፈጭም እዝዮ ስፈትልም እዝዮ
ጀርባዮ ተላጠ፣ ናሙረድ ማሙዮ

የማሙዮ እናት፣ ቶሎ ነይለት
ወቱቱን በጉያ ጻቦውን በእህያ ይዘሸለት

ልጇ ደህና እደር ከእባትህ እደር
ኡሹሩሩ ማሞ ኩሹሩሩ

155

Sub-Sahara Africa

I've Come to See You

THE music of Africa south of the Sahara has evolved largely on its own. The influence of this music has been great, though it is essentially a folk music. There is no system of notation and the music is passed on orally. Most African music has a value above and beyond pure listening pleasure. It is intended to accompany many other activities. It is used in religious ceremonies and for ritual and social dances. Since most tribes do not have a written history, songs pass on the myths and stories of the tribal past. Best known of the African instruments are the many kinds of drums, especially the "talking drums," which send news and messages in a surprisingly quick communications network. The drum is best known because it is the rhythm of African music which is its most special characteristic; but many others—stringed instruments, flutes, xylophones, and horns—are widely used. Together with sculpture and the dance, African music reflects the unity of tribe and family life, and it is directly related to the pre-Christian religions which still survive there in many areas.

MANY of the tribes of the Ivory Coast, the Adioukrou among them, have a social system based on matrilinear descent, i.e., the wife's brother has more authority than the husband, and it is her children who are her brother's heirs. The wife holds social and religious powers far in excess of those allowed to her southern cousins. In such a system, the husband's status is, for the husband, always a matter of some uncertainty. This is one of the few African lullabies which seem to call for a male singer. The tone of hopeful expectation and doubt of a father over his son or daughter is subtly reinforced by the cumulative effect of the repeated cadences. This song is in the Dida language.

I'VE COME TO SEE YOU

I've come to see you,
I've come to see you,
I've come to see you Keteku,
I've come to see you Keteku,
I don't know
What you have for me.

MA MO ME KNEN

Ma mo me knen
Ma mo me knen
Mo me knen keteku
Mo me knen keteku
Ma mo me knen keteku
Ma mo me knen

159

Whose Child Is This Baby?

AKAN is a group name for several tribes living in the rain forest vicinity of southern Ghana. These tribes, like so many on the continent, enjoy music and use it in many phases of life. Many of their songs are accompanied either by the rhythmic hand-clapping of the singers or with instruments: the gong (*adawura* or *dawur*), iron clappers (*mfirekyiwa*), beaded gourd (*adankum*), ringed-rim calabash (*ayewa wosawosa*), tambourine drum (*kyen*) and the tom-tom (*dondo*). In this song there are two symbols of wealth and good fortune—the palm tree and the sheep of the father. The palm is vital to the domestic economy, supplying the staple cooking oil. Cattle and sheep are the standards of wealth and social standing. Their number is of the utmost importance in many transactions including the bartering for a bride.

160

WHOSE CHILD IS THIS BABY?

Whose child is this baby?
Father Kwesi's child.
Take him to the palm tree.
Thorns are down the palm.
Take him down the tall tree.
'Twill fall on my baby, baby, baby.

Repeat

What a lot of sheep has father!
What a lot in his own farm!
'Way! 'way! baa!
'Way! 'way! baa! baa! baa!

OBA YI, WOANA BA A?

Oba yi, woana ba a?
Egya Kwesi ba a.
Wonye no nko abe ase
Abe ase wo nsoe
Wonye no nko onyaa ase
Onyaa bobu abo m'ba, 'bom'ba, 'bom'ba

W'egya ne ban mu nguan nko'i?
W'egya ne ban mu nguan
Chtwi! chtwi! mbaa!
Chtwi! chtwi! mbaa! mbaa! mbaa!

O Do Not Cry

THE Yorubas occupy the western section of the Federal Republic of Nigeria. They total some six million people, making them the third largest ethnic group of that country. They live in both the rural and urban regions. The Yoruba language has many dialects which are different enough from one another so as to be noticeable when one moves from community to community. Attempts are being made to establish a script for the Yoruba language, but at present it is still being written in a system using the Latin alphabet as laid down by Archbishop Crowther, who was himself of Yoruba descent. In general, the Yorubas are an industrious people engaging in many occupations ranging from agriculture and fishing to responsible administrative, scientific, technical and executive posts in both business and government.

Back to first temp—softly fading

pe b'o-su pa, e -pa.   *Oto, o -mo mi, omo mi o - to.*

O DO NOT CRY

O do not cry, my little treasure.
O do not cry, my little treasure,
For here is your mother,
O do not cry, my little loved one,
For here is your mother,
O do not cry, my little treasure.

   Chorus:

Dear children come,
Gather 'round me
Like stars' round the moon, dear moon.

O hush-a-bye, my little treasure.
O hush-a-bye, my little treasure,
For here is your father,
O hush-a-bye, my little loved one,
For here is your father,
O hush-a-bye, my little treasure.

   Chorus:

Dear children come,
Gather 'round me
Like stars 'round the moon, dear moon.

YEKE, OMO MI

Yeke, omo mi, omo mi yeke.
Yeke, omo mi, omo mi yeke,
Emi ni iya re,
Yeke omo mi, omo mi yeke,
Emi ni iya re,
Yeke omo mi, omo mi yeke.

   Chorus:

E pe bomi omo,
Gege birawo
Ti pe b'osupa, e pa.

Oto, omo mi, omo mi oto.
Oto, omo mi, omo mi oto,
Emi ni baba re,
Oto omo mi, omo mi oto,
Emi ni baba re,
Oto omo mi, omo mi oto.

   Chorus:

E pe bomi omo,
Gege birawo
Ti pe b'osupa, e pa.

My Child, Do Not Cry

IT is impossible to underestimate the deep, almost cosmological significance which the home village holds for the Congolese native. In this joyful lullaby of the Tshokwe, a mother remembers her return to the rain forests and village of her birth. This return marked a reintegration with natural world order and a consequent new-found fertility. The imploring urgency of this lullaby urges the child not to disrupt the newly reestablished chain of being of which the child itself is an exemplar. The Tshokwe (a sub-tribe of the Bantus) speak one or another dialect of the Swahili language. They inhabit the tropical rain forest in which the village of Manguya is situated. Nearby Shapoke is located on the grassy savannah lands.

Tshokwe Tribe

REFRAIN

ma - kongi -ditshe he Ma - ma kon -gi -dit -shi he _____
Ma - ma Mni -i -kau -an hae. _____

MY CHILD, DO NOT CRY

My child, do not cry. Don't cry, my child.
When I was in the village of Shapoke
I was very sad
Because I could have no child.
But now that I am in Manguya
I have had you.
So do not spoil my joy in having you
By continuing to cry so.
By continuing to cry so.

TSHAMBA MUANA

Tshamba muana, Mama Tshamba he
Tshamba muana nguna biye
Mopoke te lamba na mona hé
Tshamba muana ngukese Manguya
Na sema Tshamu tshimbi mbu
Tshamutshimbi Tshatamba kuhamba kukolesa mbu
Mama kongiditshe he
Mama kongiditshi he
Mama Mniikauanhae.

Abiyoyo

THIS haunting song first came to the attention of the European public at large in a BBC broadcast of a program of South African folk music, performed by an eight-voice choir from St. Matthew's College of Cape Province. The words have no translatable meaning, being purely onomatopoetic. The song comes at the conclusion of a bedtime story which involves a threatening monster. The children are given a charm to protect them and they are inspired to sing this hypnotic song. The rhythm affects the monster and forces him to dance to it. Thus he can be quickly dispensed with by the parents while the children gradually fall asleep.

ABIYOYO

Abiyoyo abiyoyo
Abiyoyo abiyoyo
Abiyoyo, yo, yo, yo biyoyo
Abiyoyo yo, yo, yo
Biyoyo

O Hush Thee, Baby

IN the darkening African night, a mother has left her child with another woman, perhaps with a sister or with a grandmother, or perhaps with another mother in the polygamous Zulu household. The child is crying and the woman can only comfort it with a promise that the mother will soon return bringing pretty berries. The lullaby she sings has the character of a bird song. It may be that she is trying to imitate one of the songsters so numerous in this South African country. The Zulus live in the Province of Natal which borders on the Indian Ocean. The climate is favorable to farming and cattle raising. They are but one of a very large family of Negro tribes known as the Bantus. The languages and dialects of these tribes are many. The Zulu's language is also called Zulu and is written in the Latin script.

O HUSH THEE, BABY

O hush thee, baby, O hush thee!
Thy mother is not with thee,
She tarried in the hills.
The zig-zag trail hath held her, Iwa!
O hush thee, baby, O hush thee!
Thy mother soon is coming,
She'll bring thee pretty berries, Iwa!

O TULA, MNTWANA

O tula, mntwana, O tula!
Unyokp aka mukp,
Usele 'zintaben.
Uhlushwa izigwegwe, Iwa!
O tula, mntwana, O tula!
Unyoko o zezobuya,
A k'patele into enhle, Iwa!

Hush, Hush, Hush Child

THE Cewa, a sub-tribe of the Maravi, now inhabit the land surrounding Lake Malawi (formerly Lake Nyasa). When Nyasaland achieved independence in 1964, it reverted to its indigenous name Malawi. According to an ancient folk legend, these people were once nomadic wanderers aimlessly traversing the face of Africa until they came to the edge of the high northern plateau and saw shimmering beneath them a broad lake brilliant in the sunlight. They called the lake Malawi, which in Chi-Nyanja, their native tongue, means flames, and decided to settle along its fertile shores. They became known as "the people of the flames." Cewa women often sing this lullaby as they carry their children on their backs, or as they nurse them swaying from side to side.

HUSH, HUSH, HUSH CHILD

Hush, hush, hush child.
When I go for water, the child is on my back.
When I go for firewood, the child is on my back.
When I go to the fields, the child is on my back.
When I cook, move away, over there,
Child of someone else,
Or I may burn you,
And that would make them grumble for a long time.
Hush.

ALULU ALULU ALULU MWANA

Alulu, alulu, alulu mwana.
Kumadzi ndinkanaye.
Kunkhuni ndinkanaye.
Kumunda ndinkanaye.
Pophika sendera uko,
Mwana wamwini,
Ndingakutente,
Kulongolola kulipatali.
Alululu.

O Son, Son

THIS lullaby is sung by the Wanyakyusa and Wabunga tribes in the Rungwa Valley district south of Lake Tanganyika. On the eastern shore of that famed lake is Ujiji, where Dr. David Livingston met Sir Henry M. Stanley more than a century ago, and to the northeast towers Mount Kilimanjaro, the tallest peak in Africa. Crowned with ghostly snow throughout the year, tall against the blue sky, it has inspired among natives throughout the whole region the belief that it is the dwelling place of the Divine Spirit. This plaintive little lullaby takes the form of a confession. The child has evidently broken his father's pipe, made from the bottle-shaped gourd called calabash. There are gourds large enough to cover and protect an infant from the blistering sun, while being carried on the mother's back as she goes about her various chores.

O SON, SON

O son, son,
Where are you, where are you, where are you?
Mother, mother,
I am here, I am here, I am here.
I have broken the calabash
Of my father, of my father, of my father.

MWANA MWANA

Mwana, mwana
Ulikugu, ulikugu, ulikugu?
Juba, juba,
Ndikuno, ndikuno, ndikuno.
Ngogile kafulu
Katati, katati, katati.

169

Child of Mine, Hush!

KABAKA (or King) Edward William Fredrick David Walugembe Mutebi Luwangula Mutesa, His Highness Mutesa the Second, known more familiarly to his good friends as "Freddie," rules Buganda, the largest and most important province of Uganda. For centuries his ancestors have been hereditary monarchs of a province which possesses, along with considerable material wealth, some of the world's most striking scenery. Lake Victoria, fed by the snows of the distant mountains, is the source of the mighty Nile River which flows to the north over the cascades of Murchison Falls and into the stagnant green papyrus swamps before continuing on its monumental journey to the Mediterranean. This lullaby, common to most of Uganda, is as old as King Freddie's ancestry. The line concerning the lamb smoking tobacco is supposed to be as realistic as the line in our own nursery rhyme about the cow jumping over the moon.

Kye nnaalya – ko nnaakutere – ke – ra. Baa! a- kaliga kany wa ta – ba

Baa! a kaliga mwana weeba ke! Baa! a kaliga mwana weeba ke!

CHILD OF MINE, HUSH!

Child of mine, hush.
Baa! the little lamb smokes tobacco.
Mother will return, will hush you.
Baa! the little lamb smokes tobacco.
Father is here, hush!
Baa! the little lamb smokes tobacco.
Of that which I eat, I'll give you a portion.
Baa! the little lamb smokes tobacco.
Baa! little lamb, child sleep!
Baa! little lamb, child sleep!

MWANA WANGE WEESERIKIRE

Mwana wange weeserikire.
Baa! akaliga kanywa taba.
Mama nadda naakusirisa.
Baa! akaliga kanywa taba.
Tata gyali naakusirisa.
Baa! akaliga kanywa taba.
Kye nnaalyako nnaakuterekera.
Baa! akaliga kanywa taba.
Baa! akaliga mwana weebake!
Baa! akaliga mwana weebake!

Baltic

Lullaby, My Jamie

LIKE the neighboring Lithuanians, the Latvians are a Slavic people who settled on the eastern shores of the Baltic in pre-historic tribal days. Their history has been particularly stormy, and many invaders have left their imprint upon Latvian folklore and music. Much of the folklore and many of the songs, called *Dainas,* have been carefully collected and preserved. The Latvians are noted for their singing. No celebration of birth, no wedding or festival, in fact, no formal gathering is considered complete unless there is singing. Every few years there is a national singing festival and a great chorus from all over the land gathers in Riga to sing Latvian folksongs. Ballet and opera have long been a part of the cultural life in Latvia. Richard Wagner, appointed conductor of the Riga Opera House in 1836, composed the first half of his *Rienzi* during his stay there.

LULLABY, MY JAMIE

Lullaby, my Jamie,
Softly sleep my child,
Sister quietly rocks you,
Light her hands and mild.

Snow-white lambs for Jamie,
All kinds for your own,
Curly, bobtailed, longtailed,
When a man you're grown.

To your christening, three steeds
Drove we all the way.
God grant six fine horses
James may drive one day.

AIJA, ANZIT, AIJA

Aija, Anzit, aija,
Salda meedsina;
Mahsin tewi schuhpos
Weeglam rozinam.

Augs trejadas awis
Manam Anzischam,
Strupj-un garastites,
Sprogainites ar'!

Trejeem sirgeem brauza
Tawas krustibas.
Deews dod Anzischami
Sescheem sirgeem braukt.

175

Fall Asleep, Little One

ESTONIA is half the size of Indiana and lies across the bay from Finland on the Baltic Sea. Its people are related to the Finns, belonging to the Ural-Altaic ethnic group. They have been settled in this area for thousands of years. The Estonians are especially noted for their love of poetry and for their great skill in improvising poems of all kinds for all occasions.

With this tradition of poetic skill goes a great interest in song. Their folk music is rich in native elements and borrowing from neighboring cultures. A great effort has been made to preserve the store of Estonian folklore and music. Thanks to a small dedicated group, a fine collection is now housed in the archives of Tartu University, located in the Estonian city of that name.

MODERATO TENDERAMENTE

Tu — du, mu ti – pa – ke, Tu – du, mu ta – pa – ke, Laande laks puh – ke – le päi – ke, Pe – sas – se lin – nuke väi – ke. Häl- li – ka ti – pa – ke, Häl-li,- mu ta – pa – ke Häl-li,- mu ta – pa – ke U – ne – le.

FALL ASLEEP, LITTLE ONE

Fall asleep, little one,
Fall asleep, my own pet.
The sun has set in the West,
    And the birds are back in their nests.
To bed my little one,
To bed, my dearest one.
Fall asleep, my dear one.
Sleep, oh! sleep.

Close your eyes, little one,
Close your eyes, my own pet.
The sun and the birds have
    Fallen asleep to the wind's lullaby.
Mother is singing now,
Mother is singing low.
Fall asleep my dear one.
Sleep, oh! sleep.

Close your eyes, my dear one,
Close your eyes, my own pet.
Birds will arise and
    Awaken the sun with their lovely song.
You will awaken too,
You will arise my pet.
Rise up to play again.
Play, till dusk.

TU-DU, MU TIPAKE

Tu-du, mu tipake,
Tu-du, mu tapake,
Laande laks puhkele päike,
    Pesasse linnuke väike.
Hälli ka tipake,
Hälli ka tapake
Hälli, mu tapake
Unele.

Ui-nu, mu tipake,
Ui-nu, mu tapake,
Tuul laulis magama päikse,
    Magama linnukee väikse.
Laulab ka emake,
Laulab ka emake
Ui-nu, mu tipake
Unele.

Tu-du, mu tipake,
Tu-du, mu tapake,
Hommikul tõuseb siis päike
    Siristab linnuke väike.
Touseb ka ülesse,
Touseb ka ülesse
Tillu, mu tipake
Mängule.

Tu-Tu-Tu-Ti Little One

THE character of the Finns is described by their own word, *Sisu,* which means solid and rock-like and, metaphorically, enduring and courageous. Finland has been a battleground for other nations over the centuries, but the Finns have always managed somehow to regain their independence, even against apparently overwhelming odds. Finland is called "the land of the thousand lakes" and includes vast lonely stretches of forest and moor. Scenery and climate play an important part in their folklore, poetry, and song. The songs, called *runes,* are often accompanied by the *kantele,* a folk instrument of ancient origin with as many as 20 or 30 strings. The Finnish language, like the related Hungarian, is one of the remaining branches of Finno-Ugrian, a language rich in vowel sounds and possessing a naturally melodious quality which lends itself to song.

Tuu-tuu-tuu – ti   pie - noista!   Nu – ku ar – maani   rau - hassa;

Täh-det tuol – la   tai – vaala   Kaik – ki lap – sen   lam - paita,

Kuu on heil – lä   pai-menna   Nu – ku ar – mas   rau – – hassa.

TU-TU-TU-TI LITTLE ONE

Tu, tu, tu, ti little one,
Sleep in peace, precious little one.
High above the stars are lambs,
The shining moon their shepherd.
Off to sleep now, little one,
Sleep my precious, dearest little one.

Now then sleep, tu, tu, tu, ti
Rosy-cheeked and mouth so smiling,
May you always tread the good path.
Then you the children will follow,
So to sleep, sleep, little one,
Sleep my precious, dearest little one.

Thrive and grow big dearest one,
Grow to be a fine Finnish man.
Then when Mother will grow old
Her protector you will be.
Sleep, my baby, little one,
Sleep my precious, dearest little one.

TUUTUUTI PIENOISTA!

Tuutuuti pienoista!
Nuku armaani rauhassa;
Tähdet tuolla taivaala
Kaikki lapsen lampaita,
Kuu on heillä paimenna
Nuku armas rauhassa.

Uinunyt tuutituu
Ruusuposki ja hymysuu!
Oi jos pienet jalkasi
Aina teillä kulkisi,
Missä lapsen enkeli
Ilo mielin seuraisi.

Tuutuuti peinoista!
Nuku armaani rauhassa,
Kasva, kasva suureksi,
Aimo Suomen mieheksi,
Äiti kun käy vanhaksi
Lapsi varttuu turvaksi.

179

Sleep Is Behind the Door

KARELIA, in southeast Finland, borders on Russia, and the whole province, especially the city of Viipuri, shows many signs of the Russian influence and character, also evident in this lullaby. It was here in this area and the surrounding countryside that a young man called Elias Lönnrot travelled in the early 19th century, and made friends wherever he went. He played his flute for them and they sang to him the old folksongs and told him the stories and legends hidden from most ears. In the years that followed he wrote all this down. Gradually it took shape in the epic *Kalevala* (1835). The American poet Longfellow was greatly influenced by the lyrical style and pattern of the meter, which he used in his own poem *Hiawatha*. The Finnish composer Jean Sibelius based a number of his works upon the characters and legends of the *Kalevala*.

SLEEP IS BEHIND THE DOOR

Do thou sleep, little one, sleep is behind the door,
On thy pillow, do thou go to sleep.
On thy pillow, do thou go to sleep.
In thy little cradle, do thou doze off.
A . . . .
On thy pillow do thou go to sleep.
In thy little cradle, do thou doze off.

SPI, MALYUTKA, SON ZA DVER'YU

Ty usní-ka, son, za dvér'yu,
Na podúshke ty usní,
Na podúshke ty usní,
V kolybél'ke zadremlí!...
A . . . .
Na podúshke ty usní,
V kolybél'ke zadremlí!...

Russia

Ee, Nano, Nano, Nano

GEORGIA has an ancient and dramatic history. Here came lost pagan tribes and biblical peoples, classical adventurers. Assyrians, Persians, Mongols, Greeks, and Romans, as well as refugees from far and near, came and left behind the signs and traces of their varied cultures. From pagan worship of the celestial bodies came the myth of "Great Mother Nana," Goddess of the Sun, patron of vegetation and fertility. In many of the lullabies that have survived and been preserved variations of the word—Nana, Nonai, Nanna—occur. Here an appeal is made to the healing powers of Nana, and this song is actually part of a healing ritual for a sick child. It was first notated in 1929 by Sh. M. Mshvelidze in Eastern Georgia. Georgian is the most important of the Caucasian group of languages. It has a literature that goes back to the 10th century.

EE, NANO, NANO, NANO

Ee, nano, nano, nano,
To my daughter Betsia,
Born at the time of harvesting,
Born at the time of harvesting,
K'alasao, kulasao, nane, nane,
Nano, nano, ruro, ruro, rurot'ao.

EE, NANO, NANO, NANO

Ee, nano, nano, nano,
Betsiasa k'alasao,
Samkal gachenilasao,
Samkal gachenilasao,
K'alasao, kulasao, nane, nane,
Nano, nano, ruro, ruro, rurot'ao.

ეე ნანო, ნანო, ნანო

ეე ნანო, ნანო, ნანო
ბეწიასა ქალასაო
სამკალ მარჩენილისაო
სამკალ მარჩენილისაო
ქალასაო კულასაო, ნანე, ნანე
ნანო, ნანო, რურო, რურო, რუროთაო

Bai, bai, bai, bai

WINTER is hard and long in Central Russia. As early as mid-September great flights of crows swarm into the heart of Moscow to nestle in the stone niches of the Kremlin. Icy rains follow and then come the first snows. By the end of October city and countryside alike are blanketed in snow and remain so until late April. In the far-flung villages life moves indoors, a period not unlike hibernation. The wood for the winter has been cut; cucumbers, mushrooms, and beets have been pickled, rye and wheat flour for the making of black bread have been stored. The lullaby celebrates the miracle of springtime, the sudden and extravagant wild flowers and the return of the nightingale with its beautiful song, which so joyously proclaims the spring.

F tyómnam ly- ési gnyózda vyút.

| BAI, BAI, BAI, BAI | BAI, BAI, BAI, BAI | Бай, бай, бай, бай |

Bai, bai, bai, bai,
Bayu, Olenka, my dear!
On the hillside, on the hill,
In the springtime, in the spring,
All the birds of heaven sing,
In the forest dark they nest.

Bai, bai, bai, bai,
Bayu, Olenka, my dear!
Nightingale, o nightingale,
Do not build a nest out there;
Fly, o fly into our garden,
'Neath the tow'ring, lofty eaves.

Bai, bai, bai, bai,
Bayu, Olenka, my dear!
Midst the bushes flit about,
Rip'ning berries peck and cull,
Warm your feathers in the sun,
For my Olya sing a song!

Bai, bai, bai, bai,
Bayu, Olenka, my dear!

Bai, bai, bai, bai,
Báyu, Ólinku mayú!
Shta na górki, na goryé,
O visyénnei, o poryé,
Ptíchki Bozhiye payút,
F tyómnam lyési gnyózda vyut.

Bai, bai, bai, bai,
Báyu, Ólinku mayú!
Salavéika, salavéi,
Ty gnizdá sibyé ni vei;
Prilitái ty v nash sadók,
Pad vysóki tirimók.

Bai, bai, bai, bai,
Báyu, Ólinku mayú!
Pa kustóchkam paparkhát,
Spyélykh yágat paklivát,
Sóntsim krýlyshki prigryét,
Ólyi pyésinku prapyét!

Bai, bai, bai, bai,
Báyu, Ólinku mayú!

Бай, бай, бай, бай,
Баю Оленьку мою!
Что на горке, на горе,
О весенней, о поре,
Птички Божие поют,
В тёмном лесе гнёзда вьют.

Бай, бай, бай, бай,
Баю Оленьку мою!
Соловейко, соловей,
Ты гнезда себе не вей;
Прилетай ты в наш садок,
Под высокий теремок.

Бай, бай, бай, бай,
Баю Оленьку мою!
По кусточкам попорхать,
Спелых ягод поклевать,
Солнцем крылышки пригреть,
Оле песенку пропеть!

Бай, бай, бай, бай,
Баю Оленьку мою!

Sleep, My Dear Little Son

BYELORUSSIA is a region of Russia, bordering on Poland and separated from the Ukraine by the Pripet Marshes, which have played a significant role in the history of Byelorussia. It has a Slavonic language, closely akin to Russian and Ukranian yet separate enough to be listed as one of the 120 different languages spoken in modern-day U.S.S.R. Byelorussia means White Russia. Tradition holds that the name derives from the white costumes long favored by the peasants of the region in both winter and summer. It is also possible that the name comes from the fact that the people are fair-skinned and fair-haired in contrast to their darker neighbors. Most of the songs of Byelorussia come to us through a long oral tradition. This lullaby is widely known throughout the region and is sung by townspeople as well as peasants.

A - a, ___ lyu - li, a - a, ___ lyu - li

Spi, sy - nochak mi - len' - ki, Ga - lu - bochak shy - zan' - ki. Moy sy - no - chak

bu - dze spats', A ya bu - du ka - lyk - hats'. A - - a, ___ lyu - li,

SLEEP, MY DEAR LITTLE SON

A-a, lully, a-a, lully!
Sleep, my dear little son,
My little grey-blue dove.
My little son will sleep,
And I will rock him.

A-a, lully, a-a, lully!
Why, o wind, dost thou roar?
Why dost thou not allow little
   Michael to sleep?
Sleep, my dear little son,
My little grey-blue dove.

A-a, lully, a-a, lully!
Thou wilt recall thy mother,
How she used to rock thee,
How not once in the night
She would strike up a song for thee.
A-a, lully, a-a, lully!

A-A, LYÚLI, A-A, LYÚLI

A-a, lyúli, a-a, lyúli.
Spi, synóchak mílen'ki,
Galubóchak shýzan'ki.
Moy synóchak búdze spats',
A ya búdu kalykháts'.

A-a, lyúli, a-a, lyúli.
Náshto, vétser, ty gudzísh',
Spats' Mikhás'ku ne daésh?
Spi, synóchak mílen'ki,
Galubóchak shýzan'ki.

A-a, lyúli, a-a, lyúli.
Uspómnish mátku ty svayú,
Yak tsyabé lyulyála,
Yak tabé nochchú ne raz
Pésnyu ya spyavála.
A-a, lyúli, a-a, lyúli.

А-а, люлі, а-а, люлі

А-а, люлі, а-а, люлі.
Спі, сыночак міленькі,
Галубочак шызанькі.
Мой сыночак будзе спаць,
А я буду калыхаць.

А-а, люлі, а-а, люлі.
Нашто, вецер, ты гудзішь,
Спаць Міхаську не даеш?
Спі, сыночак міленькі,
Галубочак шызанькі.

А-а, люлі, а-а, люлі.
Успомніш матку ты сваю,
Як цябе люляла,
Як табе ноччу не раз
Песню я спявала.
А-а, люлі, а-а, люлі.

187

The Rain Is Pouring

OFTEN called "the bread basket of Europe," the Ukraine is a rich agricultural land from whose rich, black soil comes a wonderful yield of wheat, sugar beets, and vegetables. Although the Ukraine is today highly industrialized as well and is an integral part of modern Russia, it preserves its own language, its own flag, and its own traditions. The Ukrainians are avid readers and are especially proud of the literary artists with Ukrainian background or heritage, such as the poet Shevchenko and the novelists Gogol and Dostoevsky. They are equally proud of their folk music. Anyone familiar with such Ukrainian folksongs as "A Mountain Tall" or "Winds Blow" will testify to the melodic beauty of their music. And there are many such lovely songs, for song has been part of the Ukrainian tradition throughout that region's long history.

THE RAIN IS POURING

The rain is pouring upon the streets in
    buckets full,
A-lully, lully,
Pouring in buckets full,

And the brother is rocking his sister,
A-lully, lully,
And the brother is rocking his sister.

Grow, grow, sister;
Mayest thou grow up big!
A-lully, lully,
Mayest thou grow up big!

When thou wilt grow up big,
Then we will give thee in marriage.
A-lully, lully,
Then we will give thee in marriage.

NA VULITSY DOZHDIK

Na vulitsy dozhdik vyadron polivait'.
Tyagey lyoli, lyoli,
Vyadrom polivait',

Da brat syastru kachait'.
Tyagey lyoli, lyoli,
Dy brat syastru kachait'.

Rasti, rasti syastra,
Dy vyrastish' bol'shaya.
Tyagey lyoli, lyoli,
Dy vyrastish' bol'shaya.

Vyrastish' bol'shaya,
Ty vydadim te zamuzh.
Tyagey lyoli, lyoli,
Da vydadim te zamuzh.

На вулицы дождик

На вулицы дождик вядром поливаить.
Тягей лёли, лёли,
Вядром поливаить,
Вядром поливаить.

Да брат сястру качаить.
Тягей лёли, лёли,
Ды брат сястру качаить.

Расти, расти сястра,
Ды вырастишь большая.
Тягей лёли, лёли,
Ды вырастишь большая.

Вырастишь большая,
Ты выдадим те замуж.
Тягей лёли, лёли,
Да выдадим те замуж.

Sleep, My Baby, Sleep, My Pretty

CIRCASSIA, home of the Don Cossacks, is an area on the northwestern slopes of the Caucasus Mountains—where Europe and Asia meet. Perhaps the worlds oldest civilizations came here and passed. It was here in 1840 that Mikhail Yuryevich Lermontov, one of Russia's celebrated and beloved poets, first heard this melody while passing through a Cossack village. He heard a mother sing her fatherless baby to sleep with this folk tune. She sang of her fears and she sang, too, of the Cossack code of honor and revenge. Keeping the melody and the sense of the words in mind, Lermontov turned it into poetry. Since then, through long usage, his words and the melody have become inseparable, yet another example of a gifted artist building upon the foundations of folk material to create something which in itself becomes part of the tradition.

MODERATO

Spi, mla-dén-ets, mói prek-rás-nyi, Bá-iush-ki-ba-iu.

Tik-ho smót-rit més-iats ias-nyi V kol-ybel tvo-iu

Stá-nu ská-zy-vat' ia ská-zi, Pés-en-ku spo-iu,

Ty drem-lí, zak-ryv-shi gláz-ki, Bá-iush-ki-ba-iu.

SLEEP, MY BABY, SLEEP, MY PRETTY

Sleep, my baby, sleep, my pretty,
Bai-ush-ki bayu,
While the moon is shining clearly
From above on you,
I will tell you many stories
And will sing to you!
Close your eyes and keep on dreaming,
Bai-ush-ki bayu!

Over stones the streaming Terek
Splashes muddy waves.
Wicked Tchetchen with his dagger
Creeps along the shore.
But your father, an old warrior,
He was stabbed in war;
Sleep my baby, do not worry,
Bai-ush-ki bayu!

You will learn yourself when ready—
Of the warrior's life;
Boldly you will set your stirrup
And will take your gun.
And your little soldier's saddle
I with silks will sew.
Sleep, my own dear child, my baby,
Bai-ush-ki bayu!

Like a hero in appearance,
But a Cossack in your heart,
I shall come to see you leaving
And you'll wave farewell.
Oh, what bitter tears of sorrow
I will shed that night!
Sleep my angel, softly, sweetly,
Bai-ush-ki bayu!

I shall grieve while waiting for you.
Pray the whole day long,
And by night I'll sit and wonder
When you will return.
For your home you may be longing
In far-off foreign lands . . .
Sleep now, darling while nothing
    troubles,
Bai-ush-ki bayu!

A holy ikon for the journey
I shall give to you.
While you pray, you must always
Hold it close to you.
And when leaving for the battle
Do remember me.
Sleep, my baby, sleep, my pretty,
Bai-ush-ki, bayu!

BAIUSHKI-BAIU

Spi, mladénets, moi prekrásnyi,
    Báiushki-baiú.
Tíkho smótrit mésiats iásnyi
    V kolybél' tvoiú
Stánu skázyvat' ia skázki,
    Pésenku spoiú,
Ty dremlí, zakrývshi glázki,
    Báiushki-baiú.

Po kamniám struitsia terek,
    Pléshchet mútnyi val,
Zloi chechén polziót na béreg,
    Tóchit svoi kinzhál,
No otéts tvoi—stáryi vóin
    Zakalión v boiu,
Spi, maliútka, bud' spokóen,
    Báiushki-baiú.

Sam uznáesh—búdet vrémia
    Bránnoe zhit'ió,
Smélo vdénesh' nógu v strémia
    I voz'miósh' ruzh'ió.
Ia sedél'tse boevóe
    Shíolkom razosh'iú
Spi, ditiá moió rodnóe,
    Báiushki-baiú.

Bogatýr' ty búdesh' s vídu
    I kazák dushói.
Provozhát' tebiá ia výidu
    Ty makhnlósh' rukói
Skól'ko gór'kikh slioz ukrádkoi
    Ia v tu noch' prol'iú
Spi, moi ángel, tíkho, sládko,
    Báiushki-baiú.

Stánu ia toskói tomít'sia,
    Bezutéshno zhdat'
Stánu tsélyi den' molít'sia,
    Po nochám gadát',
Stánu dúmat', chto skucháesh'
    Ty v chuzhóm kraiú
Spi sh poká zabót ne znáesh',
    Báiushki-baiú

Dam tebé ia na dorógu
    Obrazók sviatói,
Ty egó, moliásia Bógu,
    Stav' pered sobói,
Da, gotóvias' v boi opásnyi,
    Pómni mat' svoiú
Spi, mladénets moi prekrásnyi,
    Báiushki-baíu.

БАЮШКИ-БАЮ

Спи, младенец мой прекрасный,
    Баюшки-баю.
Тихо смотрит месяц ясный
    В колыбель твою.
Стану сказывать я сказки,
    Песенку спою;
Ты дремли, закрывши глазки,
    Баюшки-баю.

По камням струится Терек,
    Плещет мутный вал;
Злой чечен ползет на берег,
    Точит свой кинжал;
Но отец твой — старый воин,
    Закален в бою;
Спи, малютка, будь спокоен,
    Баюшки-баю.

Сам узнаешь — будет время —
    Бранное житье;
Смело вденешь ногу в стремя
    И возьмешь ружье.
Я седельце боевое
    Шелком разошью . . .
Спи, дитя мое родное,
    Баюшки-баю.

Богатырь ты будешь с виду
    И казак душой.
Провожать тебя я выйду —
    Ты махнешь рукой . . .
Сколько горьких слез украдкой
    Я в ту ночь пролью . . .
Спи, мой ангел, тихо, сладко,
    Баюшки-баю.

Стану я тоской томиться,
    Безутешно ждать;
Стану целый день молиться,
    По ночам гадать;
Стану думать, что скучаешь
    Ты в чужом краю . . .
Спи ж пока забот не знаешь,
    Баюшки-баю.

Дам тебе я на дорогу
    Образок святой;
Ты его, моляся Богу,
    Ставь перед собой;
Да, готовясь в бой опасный,
    Помни мать свою . . .
Спи, младенец мой прекрасный,
    Баюшки-баю.

191

Bye-Bye My Boy

THE *Syr Daria* recalls the ancient and violent world of Jenghis Khan, mighty emperor of the Mongols, who swept down this river with his hordes in the 13th century, plundering and laying waste to everything. They raged through the entire area of Central Asia, all of the land east of the Caspian Sea, south of Siberia, and north of Persia. Now Turkmenistan is a peaceful, pastoral land, famous for its agricultural tradition and for the pastureland of the Astrakhan steppe, where camels, horses, and sheep graze. The sheep of this region are particularly fine. The people speak Turkic and their music retains an indigenous originality to this day. The melody of this lullaby was first notated by V. Uspensky in 1934. The Russian translation was supplied by A. Globa.

BYE BYE MY BOY

Bye-bye!
My little son,
Thou wilt become a little golden fish.
The fish goes to and fro in the
    Syr Daria,
Like a moon beneath the water.
Bye-bye!

I have caught a little fish in my net;
The little fish squirms like a snake.
It has a turqouise tail,
Its scales are of topazes.
Bye-bye!

BAYU, BAYU, MAL'CHIK MOY

Báyu, báyu, mál'chik moy,
Stánesh' rýbkoy zolotóy.
Rýbka khódit v Syr-Dar'yé,
Slóvno mésyats pod vodóy.
    Báyu, báy!

V set' poymála rýbku ya;
V'yótsya rýbka, kák zmeyá.
Biryuzóvy khvóst u néy,
Iz topázov cheshuyá.
    Báyu, báy!

Баю, баю, мальчик мой

Баю, баю, мальчик мой,
Станешь рыбкой золотой.
Рыбка ходит в Сыр-Дарье,
Словно месяц под водой.
    Баю, бай!

В сеть поймала рыбку я;
Вьется рыбка, как змея.
Бирюзовый хвост у ней,
Из топазов чешуя.
    Баю, бай!

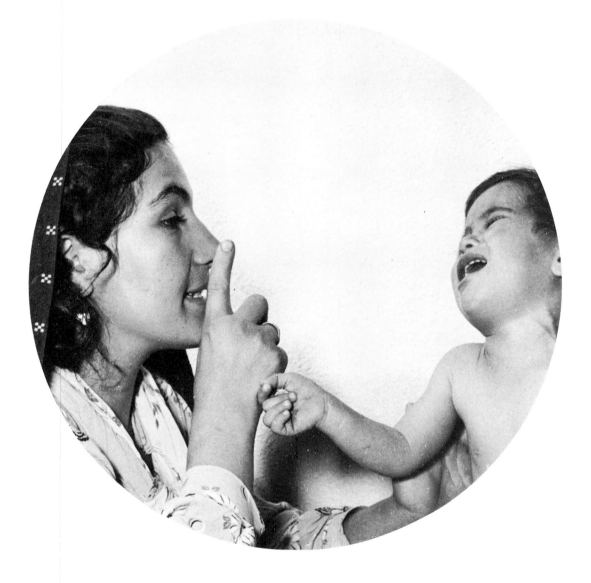

Southwest Asia

How Lovely You Are

THE Armenians are an ancient people with a culture of their own. The Armenian language is an independent member of the Indo-European family of languages. Agna, a village overlooking the famed Euphrates River, is located in what is now a part of the U.S.S.R. Centuries ago a band of displaced Armenians came from Turkey in search of a homeland and founded this village where there was water. The root word *Agn* means spring. Though the men of Agna were often forced to find work elsewhere, they upheld the tradition of exchanging letters with their families. This lullaby, in which the mother offers to fetch the moon and stars if the child will go to sleep, was first notated by the Orthodox priest, Father Komitos Vortabed, in 1904.

HOW LOVELY YOU ARE

How lovely you are, you seem to have
　　no flaws.
What shall I bring which is as flawless?
　　Hush, sleep.
Let me go and fetch the moon,
The flawless moon and the stars.
　　Hush, sleep.

How lovely you are, you seem to
　　have no flaws.
Every part of you is so dear.
　　Hush, sleep.
But you do have one flaw!
You are not sleepy, you stay awake.
　　Hush, sleep.

AGH-VOR YES

Agh-vor yes, choo-nis kha-lad.
Yer-tam ov pe-rem be kha-lad?
　　Or, or.
Yer-tam loo-soon-gan pe-rem,
Loo-soon-gan, asd-ghe-ra be-kha-lad.
　　Or, or

Agh-vor yes, choo-nis kha-lad.
Koo a-men de-gha a be-kha-lad.
　　Or, or.
Toon al kha-lad pan m'oo-nis
Coon choo-nis, ar-toon goo ge-nas.
　　Or, or.

ՕՐՕՐ ԱԿՆ

Ազւոր ես չունիս խալատ,
Երթամ ո°վ բերեմ թէ խալատ,
　　　　Օրօ՛ր,

Երթամ լուսընկան բերեմ,
Լուսուն աստղերը պէ խալատ,
　　　　Օրօ՛ր,

Ազւոր ես չունիս խալատ,
Քու ամէն տեղդդ է պէ խալատ,
　　　　Օրօ՛ր,

Դուն ալ խալատ դան մ'ունիս,
Քուն չունիս, արթուն կու կենաս։
　　　　Օրօ՛ր,

197

When My Soul Embraces You

FOR centuries the tiny area of Lebanon, facing the Mediterranean and backed by snow-capped mountains which give it its name (Lebanon means "white" in Hebrew), has been a crossroads of culture. Here the Phoenicians set forth on their voyages. Here the biblical world celebrated the beauties of the cedars of Lebanon. Romans, Greeks, and Arabs came and went, each leaving their mark in the form of ruins which dot the landscape. It is no wonder, then, that today Lebanon is a highly cosmopolitan culture, half Christian and half Islamic, essentially Arabic, yet multilingual. Its principal city Beirut is justly called "the Paris of the Mediterranean." In the villages children are greeted with music at birth, together with a noise and display of fireworks, a clamor which doubtless makes the mother's soothing lullaby more a necessity than usual.

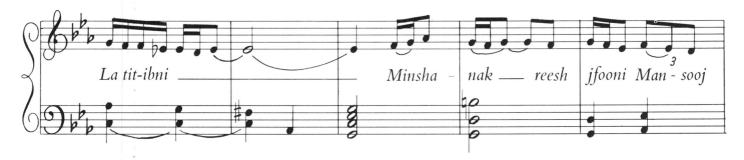

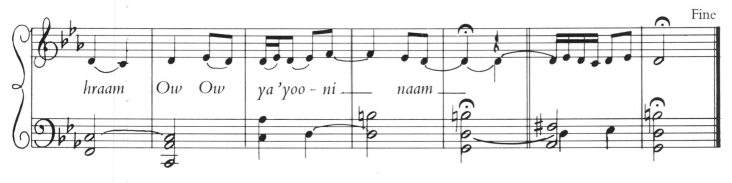

La tit-ibni ⸻ Minsha - nak ⸻ reesh jfooni Man - sooj

hraam Ow Ow ya'yoo - ni ⸻ naam ⸻

Fine

WHEN MY SOUL EMBRACES YOU　　LAMMA ROOHI BIT-DUMMAK　　اغنيـة الام

When my soul embraces you,	Lamma roohi bit-dummak	لمـا روحي نتضممـك بتزيـد هيـام
Its enchantment is increased,	Bit-zeed hayaam	يا زهرة قلبها لامـك يا عيونـي نـام
Flower of thy mother's heart,	Zahrit kalbha li-ummak	او اويـا عيونـي نام
Sleep, my love, sleep.	Ya 'yooni naam	
O-O- my love sleep.	Ow Ow ya 'yooni naam	

Don't cry my son,	La tibki tay-bakkooni	لا تبكي تيبـكونـي دخلـك ياا بنـي
I beseech thee,	Dakheelak ya ibni	بكـواتك بيهمـوني و بتعذبـني
Your weeping grieves	Bakwatak bi-himooni	
And torments me,	Wa-bit-'ath-thibni	اغفـا يا ضوغيـونـي لا تتعبنـي
Sleep, O light of my eyes,	Ighfa ya daw 'yooni	منشانك ريــش جفـوني منسوج حرام
Don't trouble me,	La tit-ibni	اواويا عيـونـي نـام
A blanket are my eye-lashes	Minshanak reesh jfooni	
Woven for thee,	Mansooj hraam	
O-O- my love sleep.	Ow Ow ya 'yooni naam	

Tonight your curls are luminous,	El-layla j' oodak ghāweeha	الليلة جعودك غاويها والكوكب غـار
The star thus disappeared,	Wal-kawkab ghaar	بســماتك عم تضويها تا صار نهـار
And your smiles shed light	Basmātak 'am tadweeha	ودارك الله يعليها و تزيد عمار
Until daylight,	Ta saar nahaar	وينميهـا ويعليهـل ريشات نعـام
May God bless you.	Wa dārak Allah ya'leeha	اواويـا عيونـي نـام
Your home may He make lofty,	Wa tzéed 'amaar	
And may he increase its bounty,	Wa yanmeeha wa ya'leeha	
With ostrich feather comfort.	Reeshaat na'aam	
O-O- my love sleep.	Ow Ow ya 'yooni naam	

Eh-e, Eh-e, Nini eh!

ISTANBUL, formerly Constantinople and before that the imperial city of Byzantium, is the jewel of Turkey. Beyond it lies the huge landscape of dry, eroded plains, the hard country of the remote villages. But this huge city, rich with relics of the past and glittering with the monumental structures of the present, sprawls on the edge of the sea and serves as the mythological gateway of east and west. By day it is one of the noisiest cities known, combining all the clatter and clamor of the modern world with all the traditional sounds of street merchants and open-air traders. By night it is almost silent, except for the occasional sound of spontaneous song-wailing, gutteral songs with few words. This lullaby shares that verbal simplicity, depending as much on repetitive sounds as upon words. For all the excitement that Istanbul offers, most of the people have their hearts in the rough and simple life of the far-away villages with their families.

EH-E, EH-E, NINI EH!

Eh-e, eh-e, nini eh!
Into the garden the calves did stray.
Gardener quickly turn them away.
They'll eat the cabbages without delay.
Eh-e ninni, ninni, ninni,
Eh-e ninni, ninni, eh!
Eh-e ninni.

DANDINI DANDINI DASTANA

Dandini dandini dastana
Danalar girmis bostana
Kov bostanci danayl
Yemesin lahanayl
Eh-e nini, eh-e nini
Eh-e nini, nini
Nini nini nini

داندینی داندینی داستانه

دانالم کیومش بوستانه
کوغ بوستانجی دانای
بمه سن لحسنه بی
ای یاوریم نننی نننی
ای یاوریم نننی نننی
ای یاوریم

200

Night Has Descended

THE ancient and still viable language of Hebrew is the official language of the relatively new state of Israel, located in what was once called Palestine, the meeting place of Africa and Asia. A young and vigorous nation with a tradition which transcends time and nationality, Israel combines modernity with the careful preservation of the past. Israeli songs reflect this, joining time-honored motives of Biblical cantillation, based upon the linking of melodic patterns, with more recent additions from both the east and the west. Native Israelis are called *Sabras,* after the cactus fruit, tough outside and tender inside. Some of the tough optimism in the face of untold difficulties is reflected in the answers given to the anxious questions in this lullaby.

NIGHT HAS DESCENDED

Night has already descended,
  night has already descended.
Where did Daddy go? To the village.
What will Daddy buy for me?
A goat and a kid.
Who will milk the goat, who?
Both of us my son.
Lu, lu, lu....

RAD HALLAILAH K'VAR

Rad hallailah k'var, rad hallailah
  k'var
L'an halach abba? El hakkfar.
Mah yikneh abba li?
Ez achat ug'di.
Mi haez yachlov, mi?
Sh'neinu v'ni.
Lu, lu, lu....

רד הלילה כבר, רד הלילה כבר

רד הלילה כבר, רד הלילה כבר
לאן הלך אבא? אל הכפר.
מה יקנה אבא לי?
עז אחת וגדי.
מי העז יחלוב, מי?
שנינו, בני.
לו, לו, לו. . . . .

201

Sleep, Sleep, My Handsome Son

THE term *Sephardim* has come to refer almost exclusively to the Jews of Spain and to their descendants around the world. This is one of the most significant ethnic groups of Judaism. Their highly developed culture flourished in Spain until pogroms and, finally, expulsion in 1492 scattered them to the Mediterranean, northern Europe, and America, where they were among the first settlers and have played a significant part ever since in American history and culture. Remarkably the *Sephardim* have managed, though far flung and widely separated, to preserve their language, Ladino, which is a fusion of Spanish and Hebrew. The emphasis on education and the preservation of tradition is illustrated in the concluding lines of this lullaby.

SLEEP, SLEEP, MY HANDSOME SON

Sleep, sleep, my handsome son.
Sleep, sleep peacefully.
Close your lovely shining eyes.
Sleep, sleep quietly.
Sleep, sleep quietly.
When you will go to school
You will learn the meaning of the Holy Script.

DURME, DURME HERMOZO HIJICO

Durme durme hermozo hijico
Durme durme con savor
Cerra tus luzios ojicos
Durme durme con savor
Durme durme con savor
A la scola tu te iras
Y La Ley t'ambezaras.

Standing Under My
Baby's Cradle

YIDDISH is an extremely flexible and cosmopolitan language used by Jews of many nationalities. It began a thousand years ago in the Rhine region, and, thus, most words dealing with daily and secular life are closely related to medieval German, while those which touch upon the religious and traditional are derived from Hebrew. The written language employs Hebrew char-

acters, but the spoken language is a lively hybrid of words and expressions from many countries. The term *Askenazim* came to be applied to Jews in Germany, and later to the Jews in Western and Central Europe. Distinguished from them are the *Sephardim*, Jews of Spanish and Portuguese extraction who speak Ladino, a dialect which merges Hebrew and Spanish.

Ei - li lu - lu lu — li, Ei - li lu - li lu — li   Unter mein kind's

vie - ge - li   Shteyt a wei - se tzi - ge - li. Di   tzigelis' gefor - en   hand – len

Rog – hen - kes mit   mand — len.   Roghenkes mit mandlen is   se – her sis, Mein

STANDING UNDER MY BABY'S CRADLE

Eili luli lu li, Eili luli lu li
Standing under my baby's cradle
Is a little white nanny-goat.
This nanny-goat has gone a-marketing
To fetch raisins and almonds for baby.
Raisins and almonds are a sheer
    delight,
'Twill make my baby healthy and
    bright.
Eili luli luli, Eili luli, lu, lu, li.

UNTER MEIN KIND'S VIEGELI

Eili lulu lu li, Eili luli lu li
Unter mein kind's viegeli
Shteyt a weise tzigeli.
Di tzigelis' geforen handlen
Roghenkes mit mandlen.
Roghenkes mit mandlen is seher sis,
Mein kind vet sein gesunt un frish.
Eili luli luli, Eili luli, lu, lu, li.

אילי לולי לו לי, אילי לולי לו לי

אילי לולי לו לי, אילי לולי לו לי
אונטער דעם קינד'ם ווינעלי
שטעהט א וואיסע צינעלי
די צינעלי'ז נעפארען האנדלען
ראשזענקעם מיט מאנדלען
ראשזענקעם מיט מאנדלען איז זעהר זים
מיין קינד וועט זיין געוונט און פריש
אילי לולי לולי, אילי לולי, לו לו, לו

Delel-loi, Delel-loi

IRAQ, with its fabled capital city of Bagdad, has long been called "the cradle of civilization." Lying between the Tigris and the Euphrates, it is reputed in legends to be the site of the Garden of Eden and the Hanging Gardens of Babylon. It is now a harsh and lonely land with a violent history. This lullaby expresses a sense of security by imagining an enemy far away, lost in the wilderness. It then moves poetically through images of increasing personal comfort, from the familiar lambskin coverlet to the rich warmth of a velvet pillow.

DELEL-LOI, DELEL-LOI

Delel-loi, delel-loi
My own son delel-loi
Your enemy is grieving
Do not fear
He is far off in the wilderness
Delel-loi, delel-loi

Delel-loi, delel-loi
My own son delel-loi
Sleep on a lambskin coverlet
Allah will protect you
As will abu Hanifa
Delel-loi, delel-loi

Delel-loi, delel-loi
My own son delel-loi
Sleep on a pillow of velvet
Allah will guard you
As will Sheikh Marouf
Delel-loi, delel-loi

DELEL-LOI, DELEL-LOI

Delel-loi, delel-loi
Ya-ibni ya al-walad delel-loi
ādoewak alil
La takhaf ya-ibni
Hoowah ba'id wa sakin al-jol
Delel-loi, delel-loi

Delel-loi, delel-loi
Ya-ibni al-walad delel-loi
Nam āla, jild al-kharouf
Allah yahrisak
Wa kathalik abu Hanifa
Delel-loi, delel-loi

Delel-loi, delel-loi
Ya ibni al-walad delel-loi
Nam āla doshak kadifa
Allah yahrisak
Wa kathalika sheikh Marouf
Delel-loi, delel-loi

دلل لوى دلل لوى

دلل لوى دلل لوى
يا ابنى يا الولد دلل لوى
عدوك عليل
لا تخاف يا ابنى
هو بعيد وساكن الجول
دلل لوى دلل لوى

دلل لوى دلل لوى
يا ابنى الولد دلل لوى
نام على جلد الخروف
الله يحرسك
وكذلك ابو حنيفه
دلل لوى دلل لوى

دلل لوى دلل لوى
يا ابنى الولد دلل لوى
نام على دوشدة قديفة
اللـه يحرسك
وكذلك الشيخ معروف
دلل لوى دلل لوى

Your Mother Loves You
as Her Soul

IRAN is the modern name for ancient Persia, fabled for its arts and culture, swept over by conquerors from east and west, along the caravan route to the Orient. It is a land of vast spaces and extremes of climate, a place where a green garden is as prized as an oasis in the desert. Our word for paradise comes from the Persian meaning a walled garden. It is a land of many different tribes, often nomadic, whose struggles for survival are compounded by their struggles with each other. This lullaby comes from the Kashkat Tribe of southern Iran, in the district of Kasharan. The language of Iran is Persian and is written in the Persi-Arabic script.

208

gu – zarad Tura qur — ban _____ mi – sh – a — — vad _____

YOUR MOTHER LOVES YOU
AS HER SOUL

Your mother loves you as her soul,
Your image never leaves her eyes.
She would sacrifice herself for you.

MĀDAR-I TU TURĀ DŪST DĀRAD
MISL-I DJĀN-I KHUDĀSH

Mādar-i tu turā dūst dārad misl-i
   djan-i khudash
Turā rūy-i chishm-i khudash
   mīguzārad
Turā qurbān mīshavad

مادر تو تورا روست رارد مثل جان خودش

مادر تو تورا روست رازد مثل جان خودش
تورا روی چشم خودش میگذارد
تورا قربان میشود

Go to Sleep, Little Child, Go to Sleep

A VISION of Eastern splendor is evoked by the imagery of the words in this lullaby. The song is well known throughout the land—a land that has from earliest times withstood the onslaught of conquerors seeking a passageway across her mountain passes to India, to Persia, and to other areas in Asia. In the northern part of Afghanistan once flourished the ancient country of Bactria, said to be the birthplace of the sage Zoroaster (600–550 B.C.). The centuries that followed his era were ridden with strife. With the coming of the Arabs in the seventh century, the

teachings of the Prophet Mohammed took deep root and still thrive. Afghanistan covers a great variety of geographic contrasts, from the snow-capped grandeur of her lofty peaks to the stark power of the brilliance of her shifting desert sands. Her music is best expressed in her native songs. When they are accompanied, such instruments as the *soranda,* the *rabab* or the *tanbor* are employed. Often a small drum called the *tablas* is used to accentuate the rhythm. This lullaby is in the Pushto language, the official language of Afghanistan, and is written in the Persi-Arabic script.

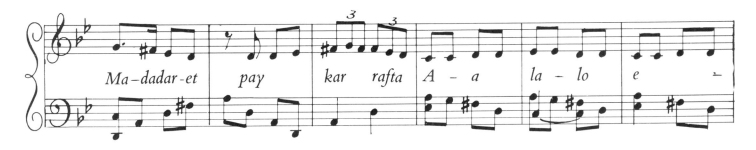

war - ah Gah - war - ah tel - ak -

ari Band - O - bar - esh mor -

wari Aa la - lo bacha la - lo

GO TO SLEEP, LITTLE CHILD, GO TO SLEEP

Go to sleep, little child, go to sleep
Go to sleep behind the little window
Your father is out hunting
Your mother is busy working
Go to sleep little moon
A little moon in the cradle
A cradle made of gold
Decorated with pearls
Go to sleep little child, go to sleep

AA LALO BACHA LALO

Aa lalo bacha lalo
Pasè darbachah lalo
Bâbait pay shekâr rafta
Mâdadaret pay kâr rafta
Aa lalo è mahpârah
Mahpârah dar gahwârah
Gahwârah telâkâri
Band—O—bâresh morwâri
Aa lalo bachah lalo

آللو بچـه للو
آللو بچـه للو
پس در بچـه للو
بابیت پـی شکار رفته
مادرت پـی کار رفتـه
آللوی مهپاره
مهپاره در گهـواره
گهـواره طلا کاری
بند و بارش مرواری
آللو بچـه للو .

211

South Asia

Sleep, Sleep My Baby

THIS little lullaby comes from Marathi country, in the western part of India, north of Goa and south of Bombay. It is in the nature of a Rig-Vedic hymn in that the melodic line supports the text with a note for each syllable. The Rig-Vedas are "Poems of Praise" and "Poems of Wisdom." These intoned poems are of utmost devotional significance and have been passed on from one person to another, from one generation to the next, over countless centuries. These are sung not only at ritual occasions and religious festivals, but also used in daily life in the home as an accompaniment to ordinary day-to-day tasks. The Marathi language is spoken by millions of people in the recently formed state of Maharashtra. The script has its roots in Sanskrit.

SLEEP, SLEEP MY BABY

Sleep, sleep my baby,
Do not then fear anyone.
Spirits bright are protecting thee,
From all evil guarding thee,
Sleep, sleep my baby.

NIJA NIJA MAJHA BALA

Nija, nija majha bala
Bhiu nako tu konala
Doot tula rakhitati
Sarva kahi varitati
Nija nija majha bala

निज निज माझ्या बाळा

निज निज माझ्या बाळा
भिरु नका तू कोणाला
हत तुला राखिताती
सर्व काही वारिताती
निज निज माझ्या बाळा

Come O Sleep

EAST PAKISTAN is a republic which was first formed in 1947. Its name was coined by Moslem students at Cambridge University in England. In Urdu, one of the languages of Pakistan, it is made up of *Pak* (spiritual purity), and *Stan* (land), with the linking *i* representing the religion of Islam. It can thus be translated as Holy Land. It is famous for its long traditions of education, culture, and the arts. The Nobel Prize winner Rabindranath Tagore was a native of this area. In a culture of villages where people live out their lives in the place where their families have lived for many generations, the tradition of storytelling is highly important. Wondrous tales of ancient maharajas and their palaces, all-seeing gods, demons, animals, birds and snakes are passed on to the children by their grandparents or by the professional storytellers who go from village to village. This lullaby conveys something of the meaning and charm of the storyteller's gift. It is in the Bengali language and employs the Bengali script.

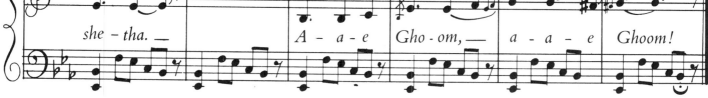

COME O SLEEP

Come O Sleep…O tender Sleep!
Mother of Sleep, come and lull my child.
In your country, O Sleep, there lives in a house Grandfather, the Teller of tales.
In that land there are many many princes and princesses,
And many many horses and elephants, kings and their palaces,
And stories of many many lands.
Come O Sleep…O tender Sleep.

O Mother of Sleep, come today, and pay a visit to our house,
And take my child this evening to the house of Grandfather, the Teller of tales.
Along with my child will also go all his little playmates,
Come on Pootool, come on Chobi, come along all of you.
Come O Sleep…O tender Sleep.

O Mother of Sleep, what would you like as a reward?
I shall give you all colourful sarees that shimmer with red and gold.
I shall give you rice and grams and even earthenware to cook in.
You are welcome to come and eat in our house on the bank of the beautiful river.
Come O Sleep…O tender sleep.

AAE GHOOM, AAE GHOOM!

Aae Ghoom, aae Ghoom!
Ghoomer Mago ektukhani ghoom dye jao.
Ghoomer deshe aache je she Golpo Dadur bari,
Rajar chele rajar konnar shethae tchora tchori;
Koto ghora koto hati koto rajar kotha
Koto bidesh koto desher golpo aache shetha.
Aae Ghoom, aae Ghoom!

Ghoomer Mago esho aajke moder bari jaio,
Shanjer belae khokonke more shethae nye jaio.
Khokoner joto khelar shathi tarao jabe shathe;
Aaere Pootool, aaere Tchobi, aaere shobai joote.
Aae Ghoom, aae Ghoom!

Ghoomer Mago ghoom dite khajna nebe koto?
Sonar moto ranga saree debo aache joto,
Chal debo, dal debo, aaro debo haari,
Noder kole rekhe kheyo, theko moder baari.
Aae Ghoom, aae Ghoom!

আয় ঘুম, আয় ঘুম

আয় ঘুম, আয় ঘুম !
ঘুমের মাগো একটুখানি ঘুম দিয়ে যাও ;
ঘুমের দেশে আছে যে সে গল্প দাদুর বাড়ী,
রাজার ছেলে রাজার কনডার সেথায় ছড়াছড়ি ;
কত ঘোড়া কত হাতী কত রাজার কথা
কত বিদেশ কত দেশের গল্প আছে সেথা ।
আয় ঘুম, আয় ঘুম !

ঘুমের মাগো এসো আজকে মোদের বাড়ী যেয়ো,
সাঁজের বেলায় খোকনকে মোর সেথায় নিয়ে যেয়ো,
খোকনের যত খেলার সাথী তারাও যাবে সাথে ;
আয়রে পুতুল, আয়রে ছবি, আয়রে সবাই জুটে ।
আয় ঘুম, আয় ঘুম !

ঘুমের মাগো ঘুম দিতে খাজনা নেবে কত ;
সোনার মত রাঙা শাড়ী দেবো আছে যত,
ঢাল দেবো, ডাল দেবো, আরো দেবো হাঁড়ি,
নদের কূলে রেখে খেয়ো থেকো মোদের বাড়ী ।
আয় ঘুম, আয় ঘুম !

217

Don't Cry, My Child

FOR centuries Goa was a Portuguese colony on the Indian continent. The result is a singular assimilation of east and west in this tiny area. Most of the inhabitants are Christians and the architecture is western. Through the Church and the parochial schools the Portuguese language and the traditions of singing and music have been grafted onto indigenous traditions. The Indo-Portuguese people are called "the Italians of the East," because of their love of music. The melody of this little lullaby shows definite European influences. The language is Konkani, which does not have a script of its own. Sometimes it is written in the Marathi script which is close to Hindi. Other times, as for example in "Don't Cry My Child," the accepted Roman script is used. St. Francis Xavier, called "the apostle of the Indies," first visited Goa in 1542 and it is there that he is buried.

DON'T CRY, MY CHILD

Don't you hear the "curu, curu"
Of the buffaloes
On their way
To the woods?

Sleep, my child, don't you cry.
Your father has gone to Bombay
To buy cakes and toys
Only for you.

Don't cry, my child.
When you will wake
You shall have beautiful things
And many sweets.

PAINNEM HALOUNK

Curú, curú, curú, rê, canam
Mouxiô geliat ranam;
Bai mojem dolanchem
Poderalea bolanchem.

Pai mojê baiêcho, Bomboi gela
Biskuti bi haddtolo;
Hal baie, dhol baie, roddumatr naka,
Tukach ti ditolo.

Mojea dhakttulea baiê dhol
Tum dholtai toxem dhol;
Tum roddum naka bai, tum roddum
    naka
Tuka ditolom goddache bol.

कुरु कुरु कुरु रें कानां

कुरु कुरु कुरु रें कानां
मॉइॉ गॅल्यात रानां
बाय मो जैं दॉळांचैं
पॉडित्याला बॉळांचैं

पाय मॉज्जैं बायेचॉं बॉम्बॉय गॅला
बिस्कुटि बी इाडतॉलॉं
टाल बाये धॉल बाये ग्रेडुमांच नाका
तुकाच ती त्तिॉलॉं

मोज्या धाकटुल्या बाये धॉल
तंधॉलताय तॉशैं धॉल
तूं रॊडुं नाका बाय, तूं रॊडुंनाका
तुका दित्तॉलॉं मॉइाचैं बॉल

219

Baby Likes His Swing
Very Much

MARWAR is one of the eighteen districts in the State of Rajasthan. Situated south and west of Delhi and adjacent to West Pakistan, this area is the traditional homeland of the Rajputs. In the caste system of India the Brahmans, teachers and priests, rank highest. Next in importance are the Rajputs, who are *kshatriya*, or warriors and rulers. It is from this caste that the greatest number of the princely families of ancient India came. They were the guardians of Hindu religion and culture. Their courts became centers of learning, Hindu chivalry and pageantry. Their histories and bardic tales are full of the clamor and clatter of ancient wars.

220

no sukha-pala su-warun Kunwarane hala-ra-lun waha-lun-re.

BABY LIKES HIS SWING VERY MUCH

Baby likes his swing very much.
  Keep quiet my child,
Darling of my heart,
  Keep quiet, keep quiet.
I shall make you sleep
  On a cot of comfort.
Keep quiet my hero,
  Don't fill your eyes with tears.
Quiet. I'll make you sleep
  On a cot of comfort.

KUNWĀRANE HALRALUN

Kunwārane halaṛalun
  Wahalunre chanorahe bal
Lārakro lāl
  Chano chano sukhapāla suwārun
Kunwārane halaralun
  Wahalunre
Chano rahe vir
  Na bharnaina nir
Chano chano sukhapāla suwārun
  Kunwārane halaralun wahalunre

कुँवारा ने हालारा लूँ

कुँवारा ने हालारा लूँ
  वाहा लूँ रे चानो राहे बाल
ताराक रो ताल, चानो चा नो
  सुखा पाला सुवरुण
कुँवारा ने हालारा लूँ
  वा का लूँ रे
चानो राके वीर, न भर नैना नीर.
  चानो चानो सुरवापाला सुवरुण
कुँवारा ने हालाहे लूँ
  वाहा लूँ हे

Lali, Keshav's Lali

PUNJAB, "the land of the five rivers," was partitioned when India and Pakistan achieved independence in 1947. Located on the northwest border, it has always been exposed to foreign invasions, a situation which is attested to by the simple fact that most of the principal cities and towns were walled and fortified and even the houses are securely built. It is here that the famous Sikhs come from (though, of course, all Punjabees are not Sikhs). The Sikhs are noted for their fine physiques, their habit of hard work, and especially for their military prowess and warlike temperament. They are bearded and wear a turban beneath which their long hair is tied in a knot. A small comb is carefully put under the hidden knot of hair, and they traditionally wear one iron bracelet on the wrist. They are supposed to be armed at all times—usually with a small dagger. Punjab is also the only major province in India where the *sari* is not a commonplace dress for women. In this lullaby "lali" is a traditional term of endearment for a little boy. Literally it means a small ruby or jewel. The proper names in the song refer to the various gods.

LALI, KESHAV'S LALI

Lali, Keshav's lali, Govind's lali,
Madhava's lali.
Lali, endless lali, flourishing lali,
Ram's lali,
Balkrishna's lali,
Gopalkrishna's lali.

LĀLI KESHAVUDA

Lāli Keshavuda lāli, Govinda lāli,
Madha vuda lāli, lāli,
Achuta lāli, Hari Hari,
Ramudiki Rama lāli, lāli,
Bālakrishna lāli, lāli,
Lāli Gopālakrishna lāli, lāli.

ਲਾਲੀ ਕੇਸ਼ਵ ਦਾ
ਲਾਲੀ ਕੇਸ਼ਵ ਦਾ ਲਾਲੀ ਗੋਵਿੰਦ
ਲਾਲੀ ਮਾਧਵ ਦਾ ਲਾਲੀ
ਦੱਤਾ ਲਾਲੀ ਹਰੀ ਹਰੀ
ਹਾਸੂਵਿਦਿ ਹਾਮਲਾਲੀ, ਲਾਲੀ
ਬਾਲਕਰਿਸ਼ਟਾ ਲਾਲੀ ਲਾਲੀ
ਲਾਲੀ, ਲਾਲੀ ਗੋਪਾਲਕਰਿਸ਼ਟਾ ਲਾਲੀ

Slumber, Little Bride

THE old custom that marriages were arranged while children were still in their cradles is attested to by this lullaby from Sindh, located in what is now West Pakistan. The melodious Sindh language is derived from Sanskrit and the script is based on the Persian script which was adopted in the middle of the nineteenth century. Sindh is especially known for its fine craftsmanship in ceramics and the art of the goldsmith. In the past no woman considered herself well dressed unless she were adorned with ornaments from the top of her head to the tips of her toes.

These traditional ornaments included the nose ring, usually in an intricate design. Some were shaped like a sunflower. Others were made in the form of a peacock feather, and all were studded with pearls and other precious stones. Some of these Sindh nose rings were intricate indeed, so heavy that long slender chains had to be attached to them, then carried across the forehead and pinned or hooked to a chignon at the nape of the neck. Of course, in modern-day India, the role of women is changing rapidly; they have adopted a more functional style of dress and jewelry is worn with discretion.

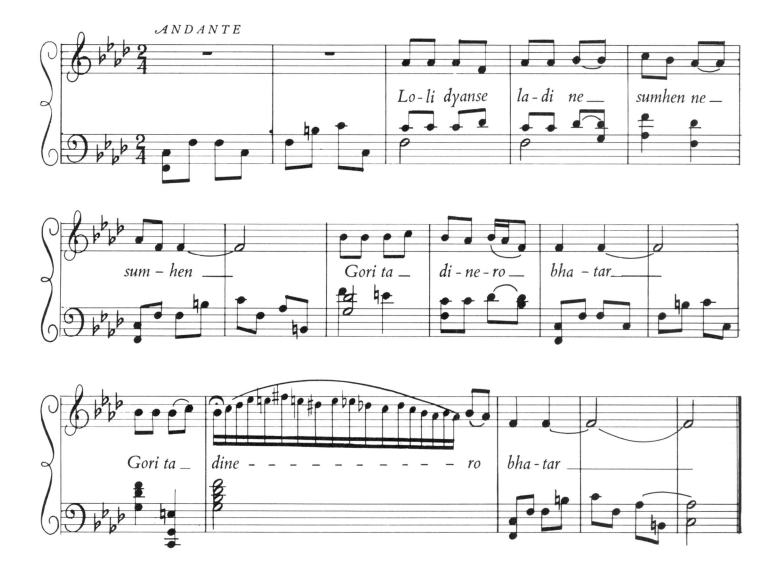

SLUMBER, LITTLE BRIDE

Slumber, little bride, who stays awake,
   who stays awake.
This beautiful little girl will have a
   husband.

Beyond the fort is a little palace,
Whence the bridegroom will come.

The bride is now attired in
   fine raiment,
For the bridegroom has arrived.

Lovingly someone exclaims,
   "bable bablera"
This beautiful little girl will have a
   husband.

LOLI DYANSE LADI

Loli dyanse ladi ne sumhen ne sumhen
Gori ta dinero bhatar

Kote puthyan ja koteri koteri
Ayase ghote gharane men

Martho dhoi ladi manya pai manya pai
Ayase ghote gharane men

Ker chave "bable bablera"
Gori ta dinero bhatar

لولي ڊيانس لاڏي نه سمهي نه سمهي

لولي ڊيانس لاڏي نه سمهي نه سمهي
گوري ته ڏنرو ڀتار

كوٽ پنيان جا كوٽري كوٽري
آيس گھوٽ گھرن ۾

مٿو ڌوئي لاڏي مٽيا پائي مٽياپائي
آيس گھوٽ گھرن ۾

كيرچئي ٻابل ٻاٻلرا
گوري ته ڏنرو ڀتار

In My Lap I'll Lay Thee

KASHMIR was once a princely state; now with Jammu, it is one of the fifteen states of India. It stands bordered by the highest mountains in the world, and almost surrounded by West Pakistan, Russia, China, and Afghanistan. Known as one of the most magnificent spots in all of India, Kashmir is celebrated for its many lakes and canals in which the mountain peaks of the Himalayas are mirrored. Between these lofty mountains and the Karakoram range lies the beautiful Vale of Kashmir. As early as 1817 its beauty and folklore were made known to us by the Irish poet Thomas Moore in his poetic tale *Lalla Rookh*. This lullaby was sung a long time ago in the home of Pandit Samsar Chand in Kashmir for Madame Ratan Devi, an Englishwoman who had spent a number of years in India gathering and taking down many native folksongs from various areas.

IN MY LAP I'LL LAY THEE

In my lap I'll lay thee, Lullay, my child!
I'll rock thee and make thee earrings!
   La—lo
Garlands I'll make thee, Marigold.
I'll rock thee and make thee earrings!
   La—lo
A feast I'll make thee, Marigold.

I'll rock thee and make thee earrings!
   La—lo
A cup I'll make thee, Marigold.
I'll rock thee and make thee earrings!
   La—lo
The moon I'll make thee, Marigold.
I'll rock thee and make thee earrings!
   La—lo

LĀLŌ LOLI MANZ ĀLARĒ

Lālō loli manz ālarē—
Gūr hō kare kanadūr garē.
   La—lo
Mālā ho garē guli-jāpharē—
Gūr hō karē kanadūr garē.
   La—lo
Sāl hō garē guli-jāpharē.

Gūr hō karē kanadūr garē.
   La—lo
Pyāl hō garē guli-jāpharē—
Gūr hō karē kanadūr garē.
   La—lo
Tsundar hō garē guli-jāpharē—
Gūr hō karē kanadūr garē.
   La—lo

لا لو لولی مانز الارے

لا لـــو لـــوٿ مـــانز الارے

گڑ ھو کارے کناڈورے گارے

ما لا ھو گارے گلی جفّارے

گر ھو کارے کنا دور گارے

سـال ھو کارے گلی جفّارے

گر ھو کارے کنا دور کارے

پیال ھو گارے گلی جفّارے

گر ھو کارے کنا دور کارے

سندر ھو گارے گلی جفّارے

گر ھو کارے کنا دور کارے

Sleep My Baby

CEYLON, which became independent in 1948, is separated from India by the Palk Strait and the Gulf of Mannar. One fifth of this pear-shaped island is covered by forests, chiefly composed of ebony, rubber, and satinwood trees. One of the legends of this land is that Adam and Eve, expelled from the Garden of Eden, chose Ceylon for their new home. This beautiful country was known to the ancient Greeks and Romans as *Taprobane* and to the Moslem traders of the Middle Ages as *Serendib*. The language of the Ceylonese is Sinhalese. It is an Indo-European language first introduced by colonists from Bengal in the 5th century B.C. Its singular script derives from the fact that for a long period it was written on palm leaves. It has great elegance. There are no capital letters, and the script is read from left to right.

Do - yi do - yi do - yi - ya ba ba Ba - yi ba - yi

ba - yi-ya ba ba _____ Na - da ___ do - yi yanna ba ba

D.S.

ba-yi ba-yi | ba - yi_ | ba-yi-ya | bayi ba-yi | ba._____

SLEEP MY BABY	DOYI DOYI DOYI DOYIYA BA BA	දෙයි දෙයි දෙගි දෙයිය බබා.
Doyi, doyi, doyi, sleep my baby.	Doyi doyi dɔyi dɔyiya ba ba	දෙයි දෙයි දෙගි දෙයිය බබා.
Bayi, bayi, bayi, hush my baby.	Bayi bayi bayi bayiya ba ba	බයි බයි බයි බයිය බබා.
Sleep, close your eyes, do not cry.	Nada doyi yanna ba ba bayi bayi	නාඩා දෙයියන්න බබා
Now hush, hush, hush, hushaby.	Bayi bayiya bayi bayi ba	බයි බයි බයි බයිය බබා.
In my darling's garden	Ba lo lee yan né vath thé	බාලොලියන් නේ වත් තේ
Two watermelons are growing,	Core madu they kuck papagath thé	කොටඩු දෙකක් පලගත්තේ
Some thorny vines 'round them twine,	Core madu they keme aaka ath thé	කොටඩු දෙකට එක අත්තේ
So I cannot pluck them, baby mine.	Kadante bari katu ath thé	කඩන්ට බැරි කටු අත්තේ.
Your mother was on her way	Numbay amm mah kirate gi yaa	නුඹේ අම්මා කිටෙ ගියා
With a pot of milk for you,	Kiri tho ganne annte gi yaa	කිරි දෝ ගෙන එන්ට ගියා
But the pot fell, alas to say,	Kiri mutt tiya gangé gi yaa	කරි මුට්ටිය ගඟේ ගියා
Into the river and drifted away.	Gangé they go din gala gi yaa	ගහ දෙගොඩින් ගලා ගියා.

Southeast Asia

High Above Is the Sun

LINKED ethnically and culturally with the peoples of the Philippines and Indonesia, the Malays are the dominant group of the Malay Peninsula. Malay is the chief among a number of languages and is written in the Persi-Arabic script. Although Malaysia is rich in industrial resources—coal, iron, tungsten, gold—and produces great quantities of rubber, rice, tea, coconuts, and pineapples, it is still essentially a village culture. In each village, called a *kampong,* the people cling fast to old beliefs. As in other parts of Southeast Asia, the buffalo is a thoroughly domesticated draft animal, used for ploughing and hauling, and is vital to the peasant family. Thus the loss of the baby buffalo is a serious matter and the mother here voices her concern.

HIGH ABOVE IS THE SUN

High above is the sun
    The baby buffalo was trapped to death
Long have I sought one
    Only now have I found another

TINGGI—TINGGI SI-MATA HARI

Tinggi—tinggi si-mata hari
    Anak kerbau mati tertambat
Sudah lama aku menchari
    Baharu ini aku mendapat

تڠکی ، تڠکی ، سی متهـــاری

تڠکی ، تڠکی ، سی متهاری
اتق کربو ماتی تر تمبت
سوده لام اکومنچاری
بهارو اینی اکو مندافت

The Storm Is Strong

IN Burma there is a great appreciation of the performing arts of drama and music. Burmese music, most of which remains unnotated as yet, is a highly developed and traditional art. Often the songs are accompanied by a harp-like instrument called the *soung* and the dulcimer-shaped *palala*. The Burmese language presents special problems. It is derived from the script of a people called the Mons or Talaings, whom the Burmese subdued in the 11th century, assimilated their culture and adapted their script. This script is composed of circles and parts of circles, originally written with a sharp point upon palm leaves. There are no capital letters and it reads from left to right. Distantly related to the Tibetan and Chinese, it is a language of monosyllables, depending on precise shadings of tone and accentuation to distinguish meanings.

LENTO, DOLCE

Refrain

moun-dain:ga. htan hcaun:ga. shan we:dhan-ga. cwei: hlain:ga. hpwei: yi: lei lei.

2.

yi: __ lei-lei: mou:bau'ka. na hpyou'ka. la lan:ta-ga. wei: lei-ga. __ qei:

3. 4.

hpo-jin:dou.yei dou. dadwei hlo-lei qapyei: she' hpwei:bwei: nei-min: hpan-wa

5.

yun:do. sha qei'pa lu. -lei: mei.yin-dhwei: hnge'ma. hnge'hpou thai'myoun hkou

Rangoon

than-hcou macwei: | qei'pi-lei:- | yanan. mahtoun | pan: wu'hmoun | pan: ngoun-hma

cwei: qei'pi-lei: | la. min: tho - ta | yaun-hci-hpya | qei'pa lu - lei: | mei.yin-dhwei:

❋ Refrain after each verse

THE STORM IS STRONG

The storm is strong, the stream in
   flood,
The whirlpools shriek, the waves
   show white,
Yi: lei-lei. yi: lei-lei:

The rain drops hurt, the sand flies
   come
The journey is far and the wind is cold
Yi: lei-lei. yi: lei-lei:

Oh my comrades, we together
Row fast in the white web of waves
Yi: lei-lei. yi: lei-lei:

The sun glimmers gold, it fades away
Sleep little boy, mother's own child
Yi: lei-lei. yi: lei-lei:

Birds, male and female, shelter in nests
Sing no more their sweet music,
   they are asleep
Yi: lei-lei. yi: lei-lei:

No more fragrance, sweet petals
   of flowers
Into buds have folded, they are asleep
Yi: lei-lei. yi: lei-lei:

The silver moon in all its colors
Sleep little boy, mother's own child
Yi: lei-lei. yi: lei-lei:

MOUN-DAIN:GA.

moun-dain:ga. htan hcaun:ga. shan
we:dhan-ga. cwei: hlain:ga. hpwei:
yi: lei-lei. yi: lei-lei:

mou:bau'ka. na hpyou'ka. la
lan:ta-ga. wei: lei-ga. qei:
yi: lei-lei. yi: lei-lei:

hpo-jin:dou.yei dou.dadwei
hlo-lei qapyei: she' hpwei:bwei:
yi: lei-lei. yi: lei-lei:

nei-min: hpan-wa yun:do. sha
qei'pa lu-lei: mei.yin-dhwei:
yi: lei-lei. yi: lei-lei:

hnge'ma. hnge'hpou
   thai'myoun-hkou
than-hcou macwei: qei'pi-lei:
yi: lei-lei. yi: lei-lei:

yanan. mahtoun pan: wu'hmoun
pan: ngoun-hma cwei: qei'pi-lei:
yi: lei-lei. yi: lei-lei:

la. min: tho-ta yaun-hci-hpya
qei'pa lu-lei: mei.yin-dhwei:
yi: lei-lei. yi: lei-lei:

မုန်တိုင်းကထန်၊ချောင်းကလျှံ၊
မုန်တိုင်းကထန်၊ချောင်းကလျှံ၊
ဝဲသံကကြေး၊လှိုင်ဖွေး၊
ရည်းလေလေ့၊ရည်းလေလေး။ ॥

ပိုးပေါက်ကနာ၊ဖြုတ်ကလာ၊
လမ်းတာကဝေး၊လေကအေး၊
ရည်းလေလေ့၊ရည်းလေလေး။ ॥

ဖော်ချင်းတို့ရေ့တို့တတွေ၊
လျှော်လေအပြေး၊ယက်ဖွေဖွေ၊
ရည်းလေလေ့၊ရည်းလေလေး။ ॥

နေမင်းဖန်ဝါ၊ယွန်းတော့ရှာ၊
အိပ်ပါလူလေး၊မွေ့ရင်သွေး၊
ရည်းလေလေ့၊ရည်းလေလေး။ ॥

ငှက်မငှက်ဖို၊သိုက်မြှိုခို၊
သံချို့မကြေး၊အိပ်ပြီလေး၊
ရည်းလေလေ့၊ရည်းလေလေး။ ॥

ယနံ့မထုံ၊ပန်းဝတ်မှုူ၊
ပန်းငုံမှာကြေး၊အိပ်ပြီလေး၊
ရည်းလေလေ့၊ရည်းလေလေး။ ॥

လမင်းသော်တာ၊ရောင်ခြည်ဖြာ၊
အိပ်ပ၊လူလေး၊မွေ့ရင်သွေး၊
ရည်းလေလေ့၊ရည်းလေလေး။ ॥

O, Dear Turtle Dove!

LAOS is hemmed in by Burma, Thailand, Cambodia, and Vietnam. The people are of Chinese extraction, descendants of migrants who fled the Mongol invasions of the 13th century. They are an extremely devout Buddhist people. Temples and pagodas abound throughout the land, and the teachings of Buddhism are reflected in characteristic respect, tolerance, and courtesy, as well as disregard for mere material affluence. They have a treasury of folksongs for all purposes and occasions. Their favorite musical instruments are the *khene* (a pipe made of bamboo), various flutes, coconut-head violins, xylophones, and gongs. The Laotian language is related to the language of the Thais. French remains the second language and is spoken everywhere.

O, DEAR TURTLE DOVE!

O, dear turtle dove!
You sing, then you fly to your nest.
Your lovely song, your lovely song
Is a joy—aah—for me to hear.

O TIAO NOK KHAO KHAN

O tiao nok khao khan
Khan lèo tiao ko bin sou hang
Dai gnin tè sieng, dai gnin tè sieng
Has fang eui, sèn vang vèng.

" โอ้ เจ้า นก เขา ขัน "
โอ้ เจ้า นก เขา ขัน
ขัน แล้ว เจ้า ก็ บิน สู่ รัง
ได้ ยิน แต่ เสียง, ได้ ยิน แต่ เสียง
เรา ฟัง, เอ๋ย, แสน วัง เวง

The Temple

THE word *thai* means free; thus Thailand is literally "Land of the Free." It is the only country in Southeast Asia which was never a colony of a European power. The Thai way of life is steeped in tradition and custom. Many customs are tinged with Hindu mythology—the worship of animals, spirits, and gods. One custom has singular charm. There is a little god called Pra-Poom who resides on the premises of most homes in a tiny, toy-size house of his own atop a post. His little house is decorated with flowers,

incense and candles. Pra-Poom guards the welfare of the family. When someone is ill, gets drafted, or wants to win in the national lottery, the family goes to Pra-Poom with offerings. There is often a feast and dancing associated with these petitions. Out of respect for this custom the Ambassador of the United States has had a Pra-Poom house installed on the Embassy grounds. Since most of the people in Thailand are Buddhists, there is hardly an area without its *Wat* (temple or shrine).

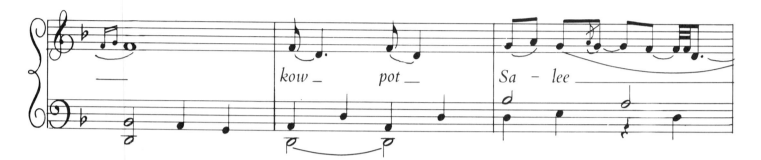

THE TEMPLE

Near the Wat named Bot
Corn is being planted, being planted.
Son-in-law will fall on hard times
If the corn will not flourish.
Then, alas! Mother-in-law will come
  And take daughter away

WAT BOT

Wat uhi wat bot uhi
Plook kow pot salee look uhi kuhi
Tok yak uhi mae yai gaw
Prak look sow nee kow pot
Salee pan cha nee
  Ja roi ra

ว้ดโบสภ์

ว้ดเอย ว้ดโบสก้
ปลูกย้าวโถธน้ สาีล
ลูกเชยตถยาก
แบ่ยวยก์พราก ลูกสททหนี่
ซ้าวโถชน่สาลี
ป่านละนี้ จะโรยรา

Lie Down, Sleep

THE Vietnamese people occupy the whole eastern coastline of the Southeast Asian peninsula, stretching from the Chinese border in the north to the Gulf of Thailand in the south. Three quarters of the people live in the valley districts. In the mountains there are a variety of tribes, among them the Black Thais. The name is confusing. They are not the same as the Thais of Thailand, though they share the language; and they are called black because of the habitual dress which distinguishes the women—a black or dark-blue tunic worn over a sheath, topped by a turban of a matching color. They wear silver ornaments, not as jewelry, but rather as a magical protection. They are a musical people; one hears them sing when they walk along the roads, going to and from market, and men and women engage in alternate chanting as they work in their rice fields.

Naun (yu) laay naun (yu), (na la) | Naun kwaang tang yan hoong samuu;

LIE DOWN, SLEEP

Lie down, sleep, lie down, lie down.
Will go to mountain rice field
And come back;
Go to paddy also.
Lie down, sleep.
Steamed rice, already cooked.
Go to mountain rice field.
Steamed chicken, already cooked.
Go to paddy, so go to sleep.
Sleep soundly.

If we don't sleep soundly
We eat sweets.
Sleep soundly.
Sleepers are spread
All over the floor
And talk for pleasure.
Sometimes, when one of us
Cannot sleep, she gets up
And begins to create
A beautiful chant.

NAUN (YU) LAP, NAUN (YU)

Naun (yu) lap, naun (yu); naun
    (yu en)
Pay hay yang hin maa (maa) loo;
Pay naa let taw nii; naun (yu)
    laa naun (yu);
(Ee ning khaw suk leew sip pay hay
    ma (lau),
Keeng kay suk leew sip pay naa maa
    (lau) naun;
Naun (yu) laay naun (yu);
Kan kauy naun kin wan ruu;
Ting kauy waa (pay waa yaang saa
    nii);
Naun (yu) laay naun (yu), (na la)
Naun kwaang tang yan hoong samuu;

Nii pen te faa (u)
Maa caw bon
Mii kuun nii leew;
Leew lian mii huan naun,
Naun kuu piin naa law liin;
Naang cang khin
Suu may hay (ya) teng (yoo);
Pau huan dian
Caang sing naun
Piing naam cauy.

"นอนเสียหนา"

นอนหลับเสียหนา
จะไปท้องนาที่บนภูเขา
แล้วจะกลับนาอีก
จะไปที่ทุ่งนาด้วย
นอนหลับเสียหนา
ช้าวหงสุกแล้ว
จะไปทุ่นาที่บนภูเขา
ไก่ต้มสุกแล้ว
จะไปทุ่งนา. หลับเสียหนา
หลับให้สนิท

ถ้านอนหลับไม่สนิท
เราจะกินชนม
นอนหลับให้สนิท
คนหลับอยู่มากมาย
นอนกันอยู่ทั่วพื้นห้อง
และนอนคุยกัน
บางตรั้งเมื่อนอนไม่หลับ
เขาลุกชืน
และเริ่มแต่งเพลงร้อง
เพลงที่ไพเราะอ่อนหวาน

Go to Sleep, Little Sister

CAMBODIA is a land of agricultural plenty compared to much of Asia. There is enough rice to go around. This fact, together with the climate and the serious practice of Buddhism, does much to explain the gentle pace of life and the indifference to material wealth that is characteristically Cambodian. Today's Cambodians, however, are the descendants of the Khmers, who once ruled over a vast empire including much of what is now Laos, Vietnam, and Thailand, and who left behind architectural wonders such as the famed city of Angkor as testimony to their greatness. Music is an important factor in Cambodian life. At the royal court music is regularly performed by one of two orchestras, one being entirely composed of women performers, the other of men only. This lullaby was notated by G. de Gironcourt in 1917 in the Province of Takeo.

LENTO SOAVEMENTE

On __ euy dek _ teov _____ Sre - y pe - ov kom yom

Tuom re-am bay ngo - um Hop he-uy de - ur leng

Interlude

GO TO SLEEP, LITTLE SISTER

Quickly go to sleep, little sister,
Last born, weep no more,
Waiting for the rice to cook,
To swallow, walk, play.

Where will little sister play?
She'll play near the sea.
The cart with its bells
Will take little dark sister.

Dear little dark-skinned sister,
Go, gather sea-water.
The frogs and crabs
Will bite little dark-skinned sister.

ON EUY DEK TEOV

On euy dek teov
Srey peov kom yom
Tuom ream bay ngoum
Hop heuy deur leng

Neang leng ema
Neang leng chit beung
Kotes kandeng
Totuol khmau bang

Khmarr euy thlay band
Teov dang tuk thlek
Ang kep king kuok
Vea kham khmarr bang

អូនអើយដេកទៅ

អូនអើយដេកទៅ

ស្រីពៅកុំយំ

ទុំរាយបាយងំ

ហូបហើយដើរលេង

នាងលេងឯណា

នាងលេងជិតបឹង

រទេះកណ្ដេង

ទទួលខ្មៅបង

ខ្មៅអើយថ្លៃបង

ទៅដង់ទឹកថ្លែក

អង្កែបគីង្គុក

វាខាំខ្មៅបង ។

Lelo Ledung

ESTABLISHED as an independent country in 1954, the Republic of Indonesia is composed of many islands, a vast archipelago surrounded by the Pacific, the Indian Ocean, and the China Sea. Though it is a land of great beauty and abundance, it is also one of the most densely populated areas on the earth, and food is a major problem. Yet the mechanics and concerns of survival, the burdens of poverty, have not destroyed an innate love of beauty and the arts, particularly the arts of drama and the dance which are a spiritual experience and considered essential to existence. The Javanese orchestra, which provides the music for both drama and dance as

well as for festivals and rituals, is particularly important. It is called the *gamelan* and includes drums, xylophones, bamboo pipes, gongs and flutes and a two-stringed violin which is usually played by the conductor. When Debussy first heard the music of the *gamelan* in the Paris Exhibition of 1889, he was haunted by its quality. Later he wrote to his friend Pierre Louys, "Do you remember the Javanese music, which expresses every meaning—and shades of meaning?" The Javanese language is akin to Indonesian. It is written both in the Javanese characters and in the Latin script. Both forms of writing are now taught in the schools.

ri Ka - ja ndas buta nggila ni La - gi nggoleki tjah na

ngis Tak le - lo le-lo lelo le-dung Tjup mene - nga anakku tjah a -

ju Tak emban slendang batik kawung Jen na-ngis mudak gawe bi - ngung.

LELO LEDUNG

Tak lelo lelo lelo ledung
Be quiet and don't keep crying,
My lovely child.
If you cry, your loveliness will
  fade away.
I hope that you will have an honorable
Life, and will be an excellent person,
Upholding your parents' name.
Be a patriot.
Don't cry, my child.
Look, the moon is rising,
Like a giant's head so dreadful,
Looking for a crying child.
Tak lelo lelo lelo ledung,
Don't keep crying, my lovely child.
I am carrying you in a kain batik
  kawung.
If you cry, I will be nervous.

LELO LEDUNG

Tak lelo lelo lelo ledung
Tjup menenga adfa pidjer nangis
Anakku sing aju rupane
Nek nangis ndak ilang ajune
Tak gadang bisa urip muljo
Dadija wanita utama
Ngluhurke asmane wong tuwa
Dadijo pendekaring bangsa
Tjup menenga anakku
Kae bulane ndadari
Kaja ndas buta nggilani
Lagi nggoleki tjah nangis
Tak lelo lelo lelo ledung
Tjup menenga anakku tjah aju
Tak emban slendang batik kawung
Jen nangis mudak gawe bingung.

245

Far East Asia

Nine of Us Have Left

MONGOL country is remote and distant to most of us. The text of this song, written in the beautiful vertical Uighur script, which reads from top to bottom, left to right, used by the Oirat peoples, adds to its strangeness to the western reader. Yet the song and the sense of it are not alien to us once we can imagine the world in which these ancient peoples live and move. The Oirat peoples are nomadic herdsmen, moving freely across the wide and virtually treeless Dzungarian steppes in the northern Sinkiang province. They have blood relatives, who use the same basic language and script, scattered across northern Asia and as far as the west bank of the Volga. But the great bulk of the Oirat live surrounded on three sides by huge mountains and bordered in the south by the Gobi Desert. Their sky is their second landscape and, thus, the nomad feels a kinship with the birds. So the pathos of the poor straggler creates the mood for this slumber song.

NINE OF US HAVE LEFT

Nine of us have left, have left
  The country in the South,
But I alone of all the others could not
  Keep pace, could not keep pace
  with them.
Oh, my noble falcon, have pity,
  Have pity on me.

The birds ahead of me have reached,
  Have reached their nests.
Those behind have already covered,
  Have already covered, half the
  distance.
Oh, my noble falcon, have pity,
  Have pity on me.

ZÜN NUTGAS YISÜLN GARLVDN

Zün nutgas yisüln,
  Garlavdn, garlavdn,
Yisn sovunas gantsarn
  Khutsrlav, khutsrlav.
Nacn songkhr, skh mini, namagan
  Avrit, avrit.

Ömn sovun üürtan
  Kürvl, kürvl,
Khöös sovun üdäsn
  Önggrv, önggrv.
Nacn songkhr, akh mini, namagan
  Avrit, avrit.

Bright, Bright the Moon

THIS lullaby, an amusing variation on the "catalogue" folk songs known throughout the world, comes from southern China in the coastal district around Canton, or, as it is officially known, Kwang-chow. This is a busy and densely populated area, famous for its river people. Moored to the banks of the Si River there is a wide variety of river craft, among them many of the flat-bottomed sailing boats called junks after the Javanese word *djong*. Some are shaped like old-fashioned Chinese shoes and are called slipper-boats or sampans. For many families these boats are home. Women go about tending to chores, and children play on the cramped decks. Song is everywhere. The men sing together while working, one man taking the lead, the others answering in the form of a musical dialogue. At night when quiet falls and the glimmer of lights from the floating homes is reflected in the water, one hears the mother's chanting song urging her child to sleep.

Maa-bin cheong, Daa nei go si-fat-jai. Gam dzao fai di Hoi fak gao gao le!

BRIGHT, BRIGHT THE MOON

Bright, bright the moon,
Shines on the earth;
On the last day of the year,
Chop up betel-nut
Betel-nut is fragrant,
Buy some ginger;
Ginger is hot,
Buy some herb;
Herbs are bitter,
Buy some offal;
Offal is fat,
Buy some cow-skin;
Cow-skin is thin,
Buy some lotus-fruit;
Lotus-fruit is sharp,
Buy a horse-whip;
A horse-whip is long,
And I'll spank your little bottom
    with it!
Now then go to sleep!

YUET GWONG GWONG

Yuet gwong gwong
Jiu dei-tong
Nin saa maan
Jaap ban-long
Ban-long heong,
Maai ji-geong;
Ji-geong laat,
Maai pou-daat;
Pou-daat fu,
Maai jue-you;
Jue-tou fei,
Maai ngau-pei;
Ngau-pei bok,
Maai lin-gok;
Lin-gok jim,
Maai maa-bin;
Maa-bin cheong,
Daa nei go si-fat-jai.
Gam dzao fai di
Hoi fak gao gao le!

月光光

月光光
照地塘
年州晚，
摘檳榔
檳榔香，
買子薑
子薑辣
買蒲達
蒲達苦，
買豬肚
豬肚肥，
買牛皮
牛皮薄，
買菱角
菱角炎，
買 馬鞭
馬鞭長
打你個屎忽仔，
嗽就快的去訓
覺覺拉！

Purple Straight-Grown Bamboo Shoot

THE family is the foundation of Chinese life, not just the immediate family, but all blood relatives and an intricate network of revered ancestors as well. Filial piety is the essence of a child's rearing. The child is the future of the family, and it is this future memorialized in an ancient custom which is referred to in "The Purple Bamboo." On the occasion of the child's first birthday, gifts are placed at random within the baby's reach. Whatever the baby reaches first is thought to indicate his profession in later life. Thus, if his hand touches the flute, he will be a musician; if a pen, a writer; if a brush, a painter; a pair of scissors, a tailor. The words of this lullaby are in Mandarin, the national language of China. Mandarin and the many dialects are tone-languages, depending on precise inflections of pitch to convey the meaning of words or syllables. Chinese belongs to the Indo-Tibetan group of languages which also includes Tibetan, Siamese (Thai), and Burmese.

ANDANTE SOAVEMENTE

I - ken tzu chu chih miao-miao Sung yü bao-bao tso kuan hsiao. Hsiao-erh tui cheng k'ou, K'ou-erh tui cheng hsiao. Hsiao chung ch'ui ch'u shih hsin tiao,

PURPLE STRAIGHT-GROWN BAMBOO SHOOT

Purple straight-grown bamboo shoot
To my pet sent for a flute.
Put it to your lips,
Lips to the flute.
From the flute new music comes,
Little treasure!
Eetee, eetee,
You've learned how!

I-KEN TZU CHU CHIH MIAO-MIAO

I-ken tzu chu chih miao-miao
Sung yü bao-bao tso kuan hsiao.
Hsiao-erh tui cheng k'ou,
K'ou-erh tui cheng hsiao.
Hsiao chung ch'ui ch'u shih hsin tiao,
Hsiao bao-bao,
Ü-ti, ü-ti,
Hsüeh hui liao!

一根紫竹直苗苗

送與寶寶做管簫

簫兒對正口

口兒對正簫

簫中吹出時新調

小寶寶

與底與底

學會了

Old Bird, Old Bird

KOREA has had many names. An early Portuguese map, printed in 1580, listed the country as *Ko-ryo*. To the Japanese it was *Chosen*, or "land of morning calm." The Chinese, in memory of the rich and powerful past, called the land The Great Kingdom of Han. And even today Korea bears two names—The Korean Peoples Republic (North Korea) and The Republic of Korea (South Korea). Through this divided land the language is the same. In the year 1445 Sai-Chong, who was Dai Wong (or Great Emperor), invented *hongul*, a 24-character alphabet which represents all the sounds of the Korean language. These people have also invented a unique form of central heating as early as the first century A.D. It is called *ondal* and uses the heat of the fireplace, extending it by means of brick and mud flues. During the day the mother binds her infant to her back as she goes about her tasks. At night, in the general room which serves the Korean family for living, dining, and sleeping, the mother lays out the sleeping mats and coverings for all the family. The melody of "Old Bird, Old Bird" is well known everywhere. *Chung-po* is a popular Korean food.

OLD BIRD, OLD BIRD

Old bird, old bird—you old
  green bird,
Do not sit down on the noktu bush.
If the noktu flowers fall on the
  ground,
Then the Jonman will go
Crying away,
Crying away.

SAEYA SAEYA

Saeya, saeya—paran saeya,
Noktu batei anji mara.
Noktu kochi toroji m'yon.

Jon po jangsa
Ulgo ganda,
Ulgo ganda.

새 아새 아 파 랑새 아
누 드 밭 에 앉 이 마 라
누 드 꽃 이 떠 러 지 ?
청 포 장수 울 고 간 다。

Sleep, Sleep, Little One, Sleep

THIS lullaby is sung in various versions in many provinces of Japan. There is a possibility for almost unlimited extension; an endless number of toys can be listed, among them, no doubt, the famous papier-mache dogs of Tokyo and the tumbling dharmas from Gumma. In this country noted for its festivals there are a great many special festivals for children. There is, of course, a celebration at the birth of a child. There are many gifts at that time. Especially important are the dolls. These are traditional gifts which are presented by the grandparents: a *hina* (meaning pretty doll) for a girl and a *musha-ningo* (a warrior or Samurai doll) for a boy. Among the other festivals for children several are note-

worthy. There is the Doll Festival for girls on March 3rd. Here dolls are dressed up in the magnificent full courtly regalia of the Emperor, the Empress and all their attendants. On May 5th there is *Tango-No-Sekku* for boys. On this day parents put up a tall pole in the garden and raise a banner representing a carp. This energetic fish symbolizes strength and vigor. A carp banner is raised for each son in the family. On November 15th there is a special festival for both boys and girls, called *Shichi-Go-San* (meaning seven-five-three). All children of those ages are dressed in their best finery and taken to the Shinto shrine. The parents offer prayers of thanksgiving and pray for the future happiness of the children.

SLEEP, SLEEP, LITTLE ONE, SLEEP

Sleep, sleep, little one, sleep.
Be good, baby, now go to sleep.

Do you know where your nurse
    has gone?
Gone to her village across the
    mountain far away.

What will she bring baby from
    yonder town?
A lovely flute and a thunder-
    sounding drum.

NEN NEN KORORIYO OKORORIYO

Nen nen kororiyo okororiyo
Bōyawa yoikoda nenneshina

Bōyano omoriwa dokoeitta
Anoyama koete satoeitta

Nēyano omiyage nani morata
Denden taikoni shō no fue

江戸子守唄

ねんねんよい子だ
ねんねしな
坊やはよい子だ
ねんねしな

坊やの子守は
どこへいつた
あの山こえて
里へいつた

里のお土産に
何もろた
でんでん太鼓に
しようの笛

Sleep, Baby, Sleep

THE nature of traditional Japanese family life makes the lullaby particularly important in that culture. It is the custom that a Japanese child never goes to bed at night alone. The child is accompanied by someone until he falls asleep. Since many generations and branches of a family are apt to live together under one roof, that someone could be the mother, grandmother, sister, aunt, cousin, or female servant; this custom still prevails. This lullaby, though found in various versions in other provinces of Japan, stems originally from Izumo in the southwest, facing on the Sea of Japan. It is a province noted for its stable prosperity and for a rich and distinctive mythology. From here came the warrior class called the *Samurai*, once a military power.

256

re   de ommi ga nagai e | sona!   Nen — ne — ko.

SLEEP, BABY, SLEEP

Sleep, baby, sleep, why does
The baby rabbit on the mountain

Have such long ears?
Have such long ears?

Before he was born
His mother ate the leaves of
    the loquat,

And ate the leaves of the
    bamboo grass.
That's why his ears are so long!

Sleep baby, sleep.

NENNEKO

Nenneko oyama no,
Usagi no ko naze mata

Omimi ga nagai e yara?
Omimi ga nagai e yara?

Okkasan no onaka ni
Oru toki ni, biwa no ha,

Sasa no ha, tabeta sona.
Sore de ommi ga nagai e sona!

Nenneko.

ねんねこ

ねんねこお山の
兎の子なぜまた

お耳が長いえやら
お耳が長いえやら

おつかさんのお腹に
ある時に枇杷の葉

笹の葉食べたそな
それでお耳が長いそな

ねんねこ

Pacific Islands

Little One, Oh Little One, Go to Sleep

THE Portuguese explorer, Ferdinand Magellan, reached the Philippines in 1521 during his attempt to circumnavigate the world. In 1565 the Spanish took possession of this archipelago and began to colonize the islands. They named it in honor of Prince Philip, then heir to the throne of Spain. The Philippines became a possession of the United States in 1898 and, following World War II, gained full independence. This is a lullaby of the Illongo Visayans who live on the island of Panay and the smaller islands nearby. The official language is Tagalog, and it belongs to the Malay-Polynesian family of languages. It is written in the Latin alphabet and has no accents.

LITTLE ONE, OH LITTLE ONE, GO TO SLEEP

Little one, oh little one, go to sleep.
Your mother is not here.
She went to buy some bread.
Little one, oh little one, go to sleep.

ILI, ILI, TULOG ANAY

Ili, ili, tulog anay.
Wala diri imong Nanay.
Kadto tienda bakal papay.
Ili, ili, tulog anay, anay, anay.

Listen to Me, You Parents

SAMOA is roughly 2300 miles southwest of the islands of Hawaii, in the vast spaces of the south Pacific. It is largely covered with tropical rain forests. This little lullaby is virtually unique in that it is addressed to the parents rather than the child—"Listen, you parents." The *siapo* mentioned is a kind of coverlet made from native fibers. Actually Samoa has a great deal more than *siapo*. Taro, bread-fruit, yams, pineapples, oranges and bananas grow in such abundance that they are exported. The Samoan language, like Tahitian and Maori, is a Polynesian language requiring but a limited alphabet. Samoan employs the Latin script.

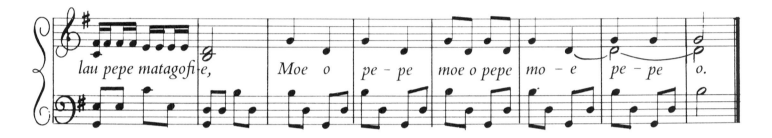

LISTEN TO ME, YOU PARENTS

Listen to me, you parents,
While I explain;
This is the way to soothe a baby,
To make it sleep while it clings to thee,
Lulled by your music.
And when it sleeps lay it down,
Cover it over with its siapo,
For Samoa has nothing else.

Chorus

Baby sleeps, my pretty baby sleeps,
Baby sleeps, my pretty baby sleeps,
Baby sleeps, baby sleeps, baby, you sleep.

FAALOGO MAI OUTOU MATUA

Faalogo mai outou matua,
Sei ou Faamatala atua;
A faapenei ona tausi le pepe,
A faamoemoe faapipii a te oe,
Malagi iai sau pese.
A moe gase tuu ilalo,
Faafui sona siapo,
Aua o Samoa e le mauoa.

Chorus

Moe o pepe moe la pepe matagofie,
Moe o pepe moe la pepe matagofie,
Moe o pepe moe o pepe moe pepe.

Sleep Baby

THOUGH Tahiti is a French possession, her language is Tahitian, a Polynesian language related to Samoan and Maori. Tahiti was visited by Captain Bligh in the *Bounty* in 1788–9. The beauty of its women and the luxuriant terrain greatly impressed Herman Melville, Paul Gauguin and Charles Darwin. Robert Louis Stevenson called Tahitians "God's sweetest works." This lullaby throws some light on the culinary specialties of the Tahitians. *Fei* is a large cooking banana used as one of the staple foods of the island. When *fei* is mixed with the native starch and cooked, the result is a pudding called *popei*, reputed to be a gourmet's delight.

SLEEP BABY

Sleep baby,
Your mother is going (for) fish,
Your father is going (up) the valley,
Going up for fei
For popoi for baby.

TAOTO BEBE

Taoto bebe,
Tera mama tei te i'a,
Tera papa tei te peho,
Te haere tura ite fei
Ei popoi na bebe.

I Hold Thee, My Baby

THE eight major volcanic islands of Hawaii were first visited by the British Captain James Cook in 1778, and they have been a haven to visitors ever since. Today people from a wide range of national and cultural backgrounds are to be found in Hawaii. The simplicity of the melody of this lullaby, so chant-like in character, may seem surprising to all who have a memory or an image of Hawaii. Rich, verdant, and utterly restful, Hawaii has long been known as the Paradise of the Pacific. But where the bounty of nature is everywhere evident in almost baroque profusion, simplicity is the right note for a restless child.

I HOLD THEE, MY BABY

I hold thee, my baby,
I hold thee, my baby.
I rock thee landwards.
I rock thee seawards.
My own child,
Rest.

E HII LEI E

E hii lei e,
Hina i uka e,
Hina i uka e.
Hina i kaie.
E kuu kama hoie,
E malie.

Though Shadows Dark

THIS lullaby comes to us from one of the most "primitive" cultures on the earth, the mysterious aborigines of the island continent of Australia, dark-skinned peoples who lived there long before the first white settlers arrived. These people, members of the Australoid race, were long a source of great curiosity to anthropologists, because they were the sole survivors of "the stone age" culture, living, it is thought, as all mankind did thousands of years ago. More recent studies have shown how remarkably well their ways of life are adapted to their natural environment; and moreover, the remarkable survival of their culture, even into the space age, is living proof of mankind's ability to adapt and to endure. For us, this little lullaby extends not only over distances but also over time, showing that mankind has always in all cultures sung its children to sleep.

THOUGH SHADOWS DARK

Though shadows dark
Fall on your bed of bark
Have no fear
For mother's near
Mn—Mn—Mn—Mn

MUMMA WAR-RANNO

Mumma War-runno
Murra Wath-unno
Mumma War-runno
Murra Wath-unno
Mn—Mn—Mn—Mn

ACKNOWLEDGMENTS

This book would not have been possible without the generous help of many people. I would like to offer them my most grateful thanks and here acknowledge a portion of my profound debt to them:

EMBASSIES
Royal Embassy of Afghanistan, Washington, D. C.
Royal Embassy of Cambodia, Washington, D. C.
Czechoslovak Embassy, Washington, D. C.
Imperial Ethiopian Government
Consulate of Haiti, New York City
Iranian Embassy, Washington, D. C.
Consulate of Ireland, New York City
Royal Embassy of Laos, Washington, D. C.
Peruvian Embassy, Washington, D. C.
Yugoslav Authors Agency, Belgrade, Yugoslavia

CANADA
Dr. Marius Barbeau, Department of Anthropology, National Museum of Canada, Ottawa, Canada
Mr. Allan Mills, folklorist, Montreal, Canada

UNITED STATES
Mr. Donald S. Klopfer, Random House, New York City
Mr. Bennett Cerf, Random House, New York City
Mr. Datus Smith, President of Franklin Book Program
Mr. John Brett-Smith, President of the Oxford University Press in the United States
Professor Joseph L. Blotner, Department of English, University of Virginia
Professor George Palmer Garrett, Writer in Residence, Department of English, University of Virginia
Professor Richard M. Ludwig, Department of English Literature, Princeton University, Princeton, New Jersey
Mr. Alexander Clark, Curator of Manuscripts, Princeton University Library
Dr. William Dix, Librarian, Princeton University Library
Gordon M. Mapes, Chief Librarian, Curtis Institute of Music, Philadelphia
Mr. Alexander D. Wainwright, Assistant Librarian for Acquisitions, Princeton University Library
Miss E. V. Weld, Reference Librarian, Princeton University Library
Dr. Guillermo Espinosa, Chief of Music Division, Pan American Union, Washington, D. C.
Mr. Louis Sheaffer, author, New York City
Dr. Calvin Claudel, College of Arts and Sciences, University of Arkansas
Professor Daniel W. Patterson, Department of English, University of North Carolina
Miss Yvette Dupuis, UNICEF (Public Information Division)
Mr. Benjamin Thompson, United Nations Publishing Service, United Nations, New York

CENTRAL AMERICA
Mr. John F. Kearney, Department of State, American Embassy, Guatemala City
Mr. Frank Traiber, U. S. Aid Missions of Guatemala, American Embassy, Guatemala City
Senor Don José Castaneda, Director of the Conservatory of Music of Guatemala, Guatemala City

WEST INDIES
HAITI: *A. Durand et Fils*, Music Publishers, Paris, France
Haitian Consulate, Washington, D. C.
JAMAICA: *Miss Daphne Bird*, Bretton Hall Training College, West Wakefield, West Riding, Yorkshire, England
PUERTO RICO: *Mrs. Frederick Woolten*, San Juan and Massachusetts
TOBAGO: *Mr. J. S. Elder*, author, Tobago and Philadelphia, Pennsylvania
TRINIDAD: *Mr. Eric Connors*, folklorist, Port-of-Spain

SOUTH AMERICA
COLOMBIA: *Senor Carlos Vega*, Buenos Aires, Brazil
ECUADOR (Quechua Indian): *Senor Josef Narciso Lema-Teran*, Asesor Indigena de la Embajada Americana Centro Ecuatoriano Norte Americano de Relaciones Culturales, Quito
Mr. Nathan Rosenfeld, B. N. C. Director, Centro Ecuatoriano Norte Americano de Relaciones Culturales, Quito
Miss Naomi Ware, Archives of Folk and Primitive Music, University of Indiana, Bloomington, Indiana
PERU: *Senor C. Arróspide de la Flor*, Lima
BRAZIL: *Mme. Elsie Houston-Peret*, musician and folklorist, New York and Paris
Professor Floyd G. Lounsbury, Department of Anthropology, Yale University, New Haven, Connecticut
Professor R. S. Willis, Department of Romance Languages, Princeton University, Princeton, New Jersey
ARGENTINA: *Senora Isabel Artez Ramón y Rivera*, folklorist, Instituto de Folklore, Caracas, Venezuela

SCANDINAVIA
EAST GREENLAND: *Professor Eric Holtved*, Copenhagen University, Denmark
Professor Joseph L. Blotner, Department of English, University of Virginia
ICELAND: *Dr. O. M. Sandvik*, Oslo, Norway
FAROE ISLANDS: *Universitets Biblioteket*, Copenhagen, Denmark
Professor Joseph L. Blotner, Department of English, University of Virginia
DENMARK: *Bernenes Musik*, The Music Division, New York Public Library, 42nd Street and Fifth Avenue, New York City

BRITISH ISLES
ISLE OF MAN: *Mr. Walter Clarke*, The Manx Museum and National Trust at Douglas, Isle of Man
SCOTLAND: *Mr. Kenneth Roberton*, Curwen & Sons, Ltd., London
Professor John MacInnes, School of Scottish Studies, University of Edinburgh
Professor David Abercrombie, Department of Phonetics, University of Edinburgh
Professor B. R. S. Megaw, School of Scottish Studies, University of Edinburgh
IRELAND: *Mr. John Swift*, Consulate General of Ireland, New York City
Professor David Greene, Department of Irish, University of Dublin
Mr. Colin D. Lochlainn, The Sign of the Three Candles, Dublin
WALES: *Sir Goronny Edwards*, F. B. A.
Dr. Ceinwen Thomas, Department of Phonetics, University College, Cardiff
Professor A. O. H. Jarman, Department of Welsh, University College, Cardiff
ENGLAND: *Mr. Kenneth Roberton*, Curwen & Sons, Ltd., London
Mr. Patrick Shulham-Shaw, Cecil Sharp House, London
B. B. C., Yalding House, London: *Miss Doreen Coyne, Mr. J. H. Davis*
Mr. J. G. N. Brown, Head of Oxford University Press, Amen House
Mr. Alan Frank, Head of Music Department, Oxford University Press
Mr. W. D. Hogarth, Head of Athlone Press, University of London
Mr. A. H. King, The Music Room, British Museum, London
Dr. Maud Karpeles, Cecil Sharp House, London
Miss Olivia Gollancz, Victor Gollancz, Ltd., Publishers, Covent Garden
English Folk Dance and Song Society, Cecil Sharp House, London
Dr. George Bolsover, Director of the School o Slavonic and East European Studies, University of London
Mr. C. Drage, School of Slavonic and East European Studies, University of London
Professor J. F. Mitchell, Chair of Contemporary English, University of Leeds

WEST EUROPE
BRITTANY: *Dr. and Mme Jacques Vallès*, Saint Saens, France
CORSICA: *Professor E. B. O. Borgerhoff*, Department of Romance Languages, Princeton University, Princeton, New Jersey

BASQUE (Pyrenees): *Countess Evelyn Martinengo-Cesaresco*, folklorist
PORTUGAL: *Professor R. S. Willis*, Department of Romance Languages, Princeton University, Princeton, New Jersey

EUROPE
NETHERLANDS (Twente): *Netherlands Information Service*, New York City
AUSTRIA: *Miss Helen Dukas*, Princeton, New Jersey
HUNGARY: *Mr. Emil Lengyel*, author, New York City
ITALY (Sicily): *Miss Maria Cimino*, Children's Room, New York Public Library, 42nd Street and Fifth Avenue, New York City

SOUTHEAST EUROPE
CROATIA: *Dr. Vinko Zganec*, Zagreb, Yugoslavia
DALMATIA: *Mrs. Philip Urbach*, London
Mrs. Vera Tavarek, School of Slavonic and East European Studies, University of London
SERBIA: *Professor Arash Bormanshinov*, Department of Slavic Languages and Literature, Princeton University, Princeton, New Jersey
B. B. C. Music Library, Yalding House, London
BULGARIA: *Miss Lucie E. N. Dobbie*, Executive Editor of the University of California Press, Berkeley, California
Professor Boris A. Kremenliev, Department of Music, University of California, Los Angeles, California
Professor Arash Bormanshinov, Department of Slavic Languages and Literature, Princeton University, Princeton, New Jersey
MONTENEGRO: *Professor Arash Bormanshinov*, Department of Slavic Languages and Literature, Princeton University, Princeton, New Jersey
RUMANIA (Moldavia): *Mr. A. L. Lloyd*, folklorist, London
Mr. Tiberiu Alexandru, Institutul de Folclor, Bucuresti, Rumania
Mr. Karl D. Uitti, Department of Romance Languages and Literature, Princeton University, Princeton, New Jersey
GREECE: *Dr. Solon Michaelides*, Thessaloniki, Greece
Mrs. Edmund Keeley, Princeton, New Jersey
Professor Richard Burgi, Department of Slavic Languages and Literature, Princeton University, Princeton, New Jersey
CYPRUS: *Mr. Theodoulos Kallinicos*, Chief Chanter, St. John's Cathedral, Micosia, Cyprus
Mrs. Edmund Keeley, Princeton, New Jersey
Professor Richard Burgi, Department of Slavic Languages and Literature, Princeton, University, Princeton, New Jersey

NORTH AFRICA
MOROCCO: *Professor Alexis Chottin*, musician and author, Rabat, Morocco
Mme René Gachet, musician, Paris, France
GRAND ATLAS (Berber): *Mme Paulette Galand-Pernet*, L'Ecole des Langues Orientales, Paris, France
IFNI: *Senor Arcadio de Larrea Palacin*, collector of *Canciones Populares de Ifni*, Madrid, Spain
TUNISIA: *Bibliothèque Musicale du Musée Guimet*, Paris, France
Librairie Orientaliste Paul Geuthner, Paris, France
ALGERIA: *M. Ph. Marcais, M. Lounis Mahfoud, Professor Louis Turco, Le Chanson du Pays*, Imprimerie Nationale Republique Francaise, Paris, France
EGYPT: *M. A. Allin*, Director, Center of Folklore, Cairo
ETHIOPIA: *Ato Ashenafi Kebede*, Director of the Ministry's School of Music of the Imperial Ethiopian Government, Addis Ababa, Ethiopia

SUB-SAHARA AFRICA
IVORY COAST (Abidjan): *Mr. Michael Bache*, U. S. Diplomatic Service, Ivory Coast
Mrs. Frank Bache, Princeton, New Jersey

GHANA (Gold Coast): *Dr. Isaac D. Riverson*, Prempeh College, Cape Coast

NIGERIA: UNICEF, United Nations, New York

CONGO (Belgian—Tshokwe Tribe): *Mme Helffer*, Musée Guimet, Paris, France

ZULULAND (Province of Natal): *Natalie Curtis, Songs and Tales from the Dark Continent* (New York: G. Schirmer, Inc.)

MALAWI (Nyasaland): *Mr. Hugh Tracy*, International Library of African Music, Johannesburg, South Africa

Mr. Zimani Kadsamira, Princeton University Graduate School, Princeton, New Jersey

TANSANIA (Tanganyika): *Father Misso*, resident of Tanzania

Mrs. Elizabeth Barnard de Lasarano, London, England

UGANDA (Buganda): *Professor A. W. Tucker*, School of Oriental and African Studies, University of London, London, England

BALTIC

LATVIA: *Breitkopf & Härtel*, Wiesbaden, Germany

ESTONIA: *Miss Livi Lepik*, Estonia House, New York City

FINLAND: *Professor Eyvind Wichmann*, Department of Physics, University, of Berkeley, California

KARELIA: *Mr. Patrick Shulham-Shaw*, Cecil Sharp House, London, England

Mr. C. Drage, School of Slavonic and East European Studies, University of London

RUSSIA

CENTRAL RUSSIA: *Professor Richard T. Burgi*, Department of Slavic Languages and Literature, Princeton University, Princeton, New Jersey

BYELORUSSIA (White Russia): *Mr. Patrick Shulham-Shaw*, Cecil Sharp House, London, England

Professor Arash Bormanshinov, Department of Slavic Languages and Literature, Princeton University, Princeton, New Jersey

UKRAINE (Province of Kursk): *Mr. Patrick Shulham-Shaw*, Cecil Sharp House, London, England

Professor Arash Bormanshinov, Department of Slavic Languages and Literature, Princeton University, Princeton, New Jersey

CIRCASSIA (South Russia): *Professor Arash Bormanshinov*, Department of Slavic Languages and Literature, Princeton University, Princeton, New Jersey

GEORGIA: *Professor David Djaparidze*, Department of Slavic Languages and Literature, Princeton University, Princeton, New Jersey.

Dr. G. Chkhikvadze, Director, Folk Music Laboratory

Dr. C. Taklakishvilli, Director, Conservatory of Music, Georgia

Dr. I. Beridze, Pro-Rector, Conservatory of Music, Georgia

TURKMENISTAN: *Mr. Patrick Shulham-Shaw*, Cecil Sharp House, London, England

Professor Arash Bormanshinov, Department of Slavic Languages and Literature, Princeton University, Princeton, New Jersey

SOUTHWEST ASIA

ARMENIA: *Mrs. Roxanne Forster*, Princeton, New Jersey

TURKEY: *Professor Perter Boratov*, Institut d'Etudes Turques, Université de Paris

Professor C. S. Mundy, School of Oriental and African Studies, University of London

LEBANON: *Miss Zahia Doughan*, Makassed College, Beyreuth, Lebanon

Professor Faälou A. Shehadi, Rutgers University, New Brunswick, New Jersey

ISRAEL: *Dr. Edith Gerson-Kiwi*, Archives for Jewish and Oriental Music, Hebrew University, Jerusalem, Israel

Dr. I. M. Levey, Murray Dodge Hall, Princeton University, Princeton, New Jersey

SEPHARDIC (Judeo-Espagnol): *Mr. Isaac Levy*, Kol-Israel Broadcasting Service, Jerusalem, Israel

IRAQ (Baghdad): *Mrs. Bahija Lovejoy*, Baghdad and Princeton, New Jersey

SOUTH ASIA

SINDH: *Mr. Bhagwan Kapoor*, artist, Sindh and Paris, France

KASHMIR: *Dr. Ishrat Z. Husain*, Population Council Fellow, Princeton University, Princeton, New Jersey

PUNJAB: *The Clarendon Press*, Oxford, England

Dr. Ranendra Kumar Bhattacharyya, Calcutta, India

RAJASTHAN (Marwar): *Professor Arnold A. Bake*, School of Oriental and African Studies, University of London

MAHARASHTRA (Kolhapur): *Dr. and Mrs. Robert Goheen, Sr.*, Princeton, New Jersey

Dr. Ranendra Kumar Bhattacharyya, Calcutta, India

GOA: *Miss Maria Eugenia de Mello*, Burnt Hills, New York

Dr. Ranendra Kumar Bhattacharyya, Calcutta, India

EAST PAKISTAN: *Mr. Rashid Ahmed*, Director General, Radio Pakistan, Karachi

Dr. Ranendra Kumar Bhattacharyya, Calcutta, India

CEYLON (Colombo): *Devar Surya Sena*, musician and folklorist, Colombo

Dr. Eustace Menais, Department of Physics, University of Wisconsin, Madison, Wisconsin

SOUTHEAST ASIA

BURMA (Rangoon): *Dr. Khin Zaw*, Rangoon

Mrs. Bonnie R. Crown, The Asian Society, New York City

Professor William S. Corwyn, Timothy Dwight College, Yale University, New Haven, Connecticut

Cecil Sharp House, London, England

Professor Arash Bormanshinov, Department of Slavic Languages and Literature, Princeton University, Princeton, New Jersey

LAOS: *Mr. Henry C. Holmes*, Hampton, Connecticut

THAILAND: *Mme. Ladda Silapabanleng*, Phakawali Institute of Music and Dance, Bangkok

Dr. David Morton, Department of Ethnomusicology, University of California, Los Angeles, California

Mr. Nuraks Israsena, Thailand and New York

CAMBODIA: *Miss Susan Conheim*, The Asian Society, New York City

His Excellency Nong Kinny, Ambassador from Cambodia, Washington, D. C.

VIETNAM: *Dr. Howard Kaufman*, folklorist, Baltimore, Maryland

Miss Naomi Ware, Archives of Folk and Primitive Music, University of Indiana, Bloomington, Indiana

Mr. Kenneth Bache, Department of State, Washington, D. C.

MALAYSIA: *Mr. Ali Munawar*, Voice of America, Washington, D. C.

INDONESIA (Djakarta): The Jang Lok, Indonesian National Commission for UNESCO, Djakarta

FAR EAST ASIA

SINKIANG PROVINCE OF CHINA (Oirat Mongol): *Mr. Paul Geunther*, Librairie Orientaliste, Bibliotheque Musicale du Musée Guimet, Paris, France

Professor Arash Bormanshinov, Department of Slavic Languages and Literature, Princeton University, Princeton, New Jersey

CHINA (Canton): *Professor G. B. Downer*, School of Oriental and African Studies, University of London, London, England

KOREA: *Dr. David Morton*, Institute of Ethnomusicology, University of California, Los Angeles, California

Mr. Donald Sur, Institute of Ethnomusicology, University of California, Los Angeles, California

JAPAN: *Professor Joji Watanuki*, Department of Sociology, University of Tokyo

AUSTRALIA

QUEENSLAND (Maranoa District): *British Information Service*, Rockefeller Center, New York City

G. Schirmer, Inc., New York City

PACIFIC ISLANDS

PHILIPPINES: *Miss Miriam Palmore*, Silliman Music Foundations, Dumquete City, Philippines

SAMOA: *Professor Barbara B. Smith*, Department of Music, University of Hawaii, Honolulu, Hawaii

TAHITI: *Professor Barbara B. Smith*, Department of Music, University of Hawaii, Honolulu, Hawaii

HAWAII: *Professor Barbara B. Smith*, Department of Music, University of Hawaii, Honolulu, Hawaii

PHOTO CREDITS: Title page, "Mother and Child" by Margot Einstein, Photo by Lotte J. Neustein; p. 1, Michael Spivak; p. 11, Elliott Erwitt, © 1967 Magnum Photos; p. 29, UNICEF; p. 41, UNICEF Photo by Ilsa Kraus; p. 51, Ken Heyman, © 1963 Magnum Photos; p. 69, Ken Heyman; p. 79, Ken Heyman, © 1963 Magnum Photos; p. 91, UNICEF; p. 107, Ken Heyman; p. 127, UNICEF; p. 143, UNICEF Photo by George Holton; p. 157, UNICEF; p. 173, Ken Heyman, © 1963 Magnum Photos; p. 181, Sovfoto; p. 195, UNICEF Photo/Winter/60; p. 213, CARE; p. 231, UNICEF; p. 247, Ken Heyman; p. 259, UNICEF Photo by Jack Ling.

Arctic Ocean

ASIA

NORTH
AMERICA

CANADA

British Columbia I (Tsimshian Indian)
British Columbia II (Tsimshian Indian)
Quebec
Halifax
Iroquois Indian

FAR EAST ASIA

Outer Mongolia (Sinkiang Province)
(South, Canton) China
(North, Peking) China
Korea
Japan (Izumo)
Japan
Indonesia (Djakarta)

UNITED STATES

New York State
Pennsylvania Dutch
Southern Appalachians
Southern United States
Louisiana (Creole)
Michigan
(Wisconsin) Ojibwa Tribe
(South Dakota) Sioux Indian
(Oklahoma) Pawnee Indian
(Arizona) Hopi Indian

SOUTHEAST ASIA

Burma
Laos
Thailand
Cambodia (Takeo)
Vietnam
Malaysia

CENTRAL AMERICA

Mexico
Yaqui Tribe—Mexico
Guatemala
Honduras
El Salvador
Nicaragua

Pacific Ocean

PACIFIC ISLANDS

Australia (Maranoa)
Philippines
Samoa
Tahiti
Hawaii

SOUTH AMERICA

Venezuela
Colombia
Ecuador (Quichua Indian)
Peru
Brazil (Paressi Indian)
Brazil
Bolivia
Uruguay
Chile
Argentina

AUSTRALIA